THE
RHYTHM
OF THE TIDE

Tales through the ages of Chichester Harbour

Chichester Harbour.

THE
RHYTHM
OF THE TIDE

Tales through the ages of Chichester Harbour

Jeremy Thomas

Phillimore

First published in 1999 by SMH Books

Reprinted 2008 by
PHILLIMORE & CO. LTD
Chichester, West Sussex, England
www.phillimore.co.uk

ISBN 978-1-86077-483-6

Typeset in 12/14pt Bembo
Printed and bound in Great Britain by
Ashford Colour Press Ltd, Gosport, Hants.

for Dinny,

my best crew

CONTENTS

LIST OF PLATES

between pp. 82 and 83

ACKNOWLEDGEMENTS

I owe thanks to many people whose influence has shaped the writing of this book:

Aunty Kay, whose cottage on the Trippet at Bosham gave me my first view of the Harbour half a century ago.

Sailing and fishing friends, who showed me how to work the tides and catch a bass.

Friends and colleagues in the Chichester Harbour Conservancy, like the late Martin Beale, who taught me to value this Area of Outstanding Natural Beauty.

Historians, including Angela Bromley-Martin, John Reger and John Pollock, who encouraged me to delve into the Harbour's past.

And to my original editor and publisher, Sandra Saer, for steering me with such friendly skill; and her successors Noel Osborne, Andrew Illes and Kate Wilks.

Particular thanks go to:

Iain McGowan for his coloured photographs of the Harbour.

Chichester's Harbour Master, John Davis, for permission to reproduce several of the drawings by Jill Dickin, which appeared in the Conservancy's publication, *Chichester Harbour: Thirteen Villages*; and for all the generous help he and his officers, especially Philip Couchman and Anne de Potier, have given me.

The Director of Fishbourne Roman Palace, David Rudkin, for his help over the Notes and for so kindly drawing the Roman coin reproduced with his permission on page xiv.

The County Archivist, Richard Childs, and Kim Leslie at the West Sussex Record Office, for allowing me to use a section of Richard Budgen's 1724 map of Sussex as an endpaper.

For permission to reproduce illustrations, I am grateful to:

Lady Scott, for line drawings from Sir Peter Scott's *THE BATTLE of the NARROW SEAS: A History of the Light Coastal Forces in the Channel and North Sea, 1939-1945* (Country Life Limited, 1945).

Mr Keith Shackleton, for line drawings by him, from his book *Wake* (Lutterworth Press, 1954).

B.T. Batsford, for a drawing from Peter Kirsch's *GALLEONS: The Great Ships of the Armada Era* (Conway Maritime, 1990).

Classic Boat Magazine and John Leather, for an outline drawing by John Leather used in an article on Southern Work Boats.

Mr Ian Harrap, for a sketch of a Hastings Lugger, in Richard Joicey's *Harbour Sketches* (The Pelham Library, Havant, 1977).

Finally, I want to thank my wife, not only for her watercolour (plate 14), which captures the spirit of the Harbour, but for all her support.

INTRODUCTION

Chichester Harbour is the hero of this story about some of the harbourside people over the years, between Roman times and the 20th century.

The historical episodes are based on fact, but most of the characters are imaginary. They say truth will out, even in historical novels. My version of what happened may not please the purists. Nevertheless, the legends woven in to it have become part of the Harbour's legacy.

Set between the episodes, are Interludes, which glimpse some of the ingredients of the Harbour's life: its tides and mud, and the living things that make the estuary their home. These elements, giving the place its quality and personality, are timeless. But they will only remain timeless if they are maintained, and that is what the Chichester Harbour Conservancy and the Harbour Trust are pledged to do.

I grew up in the Harbour, and have loved it all my life. I hope the following pages may share that feeling with you, and encourage the belief that it is a special place, worth looking after.

J.C.T.
East Lavant

PRELUDE

Low tide. At the top of the channel, the mud glistened in the sun. High summer. The spartina grass waved softly in the afternoon breeze – the So'wester: the prevailing wind that, together with the ebb and flow of the sea, gave a rhythm to the life of the Harbour.

It was nearly time for tea. In the old cottage on the Trippet, Aunty Kay was swilling out the battered metal tea pot that had presided over so many family gatherings during the holidays. Going to Aunty Kay's meant snuggling down in damp bunk beds; woodlice creeping across the lino floor in the bathroom; the grandfather clock with its soothing tick-tock in the narrow hall; the smell of old rope and canvas in the shed facing the meadow. It meant learning to swim off the Trippet at high water; feeding the ducks at the mouth of the mill stream; mud larking and, when the boys got a bit older, taking their twelve-foot dinghy, *Penguin*, down to East Head at the entrance for a picnic; digging for lug worms and catching the little school bass in the evening, off Cobnor; capsizing in the Firefly at Deep End, when the wind fought the ebb. Coming home to the cottage, gym shoes squelching, for a hot bath and high tea, with freshly baked pikelets, dripping butter.

John was busy shrimping in his favourite spot, under the little wooden bridge near the head of Schoolhouse Creek. A gravel causeway cut across the mud and saved a long walk around the foreshore. Aunty Kay said the Romans had laid its foundations with oyster shells. The shrimps liked the shade under the bridge. John went into the water up to his knees. It was cold. The mud oozed between his toes. He bent down and saw a pair of searching feelers, two black eyes on stalks, the miniature armoured segments of the carapace, and a flat tail flicking in the silt. A gigantic prawn.

Worth having. He lowered his net into the stream and pushed the wooden base along the bottom under the bridge. He levered the net up, water and mud pouring through the mesh. John turned over the weed, cockles and small pebbles left in the net. No prawn, but a silver sand eel, almost transparent, wriggling. He put the eel in his bucket, banging the net on the gravel path to get all the bits out.

That was when he found the penny. The ancient copper was encrusted. It looked as if it had been in the mud a long time. John rubbed the coin on his swimming shorts as he walked back to the cottage. He showed off the eel to his aunt, who promised to fry it for supper.

'And I found this.' He laid the coin on the table.

'It's an old penny', said Aunty Kay. 'Let's clean it up.'

She scrubbed it under the tap and the metal began to glint. The worn outline of a head appeared on one side, with a ship on the other, and around the edge, some lettering. The only letters they could make out spelt 'VIRTUS AVG.'

'I think you've found a Roman coin. It's treasure trove!'

John picked the coin up. He looked at in the palm of his hand. It felt cold, worn, smooth. That night, before he went to sleep, he wondered about his treasure.*

* See Note 1, page 15

Chapter I

ROMAN

Marcus stood on the wooden jetty, rubbing his shoulder where a sliver of the Belgic arrowhead still throbbed when the rain came in from the west. That seemed most of the time in this outpost of Empire. But he supposed he was lucky. A third of his cohort lay in that neck of the Ardennes where the tribesmen had ambushed them.

That smart-aleck young tribune, straight out of school! If he'd listened, they'd be alive today. But no. The boy had known best. No advance guard that morning. No bloody Belgae for miles. What had happened? Why the hairy beggars had crept up on them during the morning halt and carved the cohort up. That's what had happened. And the tribune – with a slit throat and the foot soldiers, shields forward, backing out of the defile on to high ground, forming a circle and keeping the little devils at bay, till the Belgae got bored and went home for the night. He was only twenty, that tribune. He had a wealthy patron in the Senate. But you had to give it to him. With a bloody rag around his throat, the kid had fought all day, gurgling orders that none of them had understood. They buried him that night, digging deep below the leaf mould so the wolves wouldn't find him.

The jetty jutted out into the river that flowed into the Fishbourne channel. It was quite deep. Even at low tide, the tubby cargo vessels that worked the Channel ports could be rowed and warped up to the piles and moored alongside to unload. The crews were a snotty lot. Would they do the unloading? Would they! Not what they signed on for, they said. What d'you have slaves for?

1

They came from all over, those sailors. When they weren't trading, they were no better than pirates. Marcus wondered often how they managed to sail those tubs all the way up from the Mediterranean. When he was a boy, he'd thought the Pillars of Hercules the end of the world. If a ship sailed through them, she tipped over the edge. But some of these ships had made the voyage and lived to show their owners a fat profit.

Marcus watched them unloading a cargo of olive oil. The Legion got through a lot of oil. None of the Romans could bear to eat their meat cooked in cow's fat, like the locals did. The oil came through Gaul overland to the Breton coast, the carriers making sure that a good many amphorae fell off the back of their carts. Then the sailors 'lost' a few more when they stowed the earthenware jars in sand in the ships' holds, before carrying the oil as ballast across the Channel. It cost him six times as much as it did back in Umbria. But you had to have oil.

It was fifteen years since Marcus had signed on; ten, since he'd come over to Britain with his Legion. The village in Umbria where he grew up was another world. He could hardly remember the boy who had been apprenticed to his uncle to learn the trade of carpentry. He was only twelve. Five years of sawdust and shavings had been enough. When the recruiting party set up their stand under the plane tree in the village square, with their horn and drum and tall stories, he had enlisted.

His uncle had cursed him – he was just starting to be useful. His mother had wept. His father had given him his old sword, the one with the nick in the blade where it had struck the visor of a Bactrian horseman.

Marcus marched away with the recruiters and when he looked back, his house had been hidden behind the cypresses. His old half-blind hound had loped behind him for a mile. But then he lost heart and sat by the roadside, howling, as his young master's scent grew fainter.

The sun was creeping down to the treeline on the western side of the creek, dazzling him. Like the time the Legion had been given a make and mend afternoon and they were swimming in that river in northern Gaul. The devil's tribesmen had thrown their spears out of the sun, killing three of his section. By the time they had swum ashore and grabbed their swords, standing naked as they were, the bastards had scampered.

How green he was, when he did his basic training at the depot outside Florence! He had marched with a draft of young soldiers across the Alps in winter and joined his unit in their camp in Brittany. The old soldier, detailed off to look after him, had taught him the basics of his trade. You needed to learn fast. The northern Gallic tribes were a treacherous bunch. Smelly too, if you had to fight hand to hand. But mostly, they went in for hit and run, avoiding pitched battles. That was the trouble. You couldn't get at them. But you had to watch them all the time, with their ambushes and night attacks, crawling on their bellies, covered in mud, right into the lines, past the sentries and stabbing the troops with their long knives as they slept. We buried our people in their blankets: they were easier to carry that way.

It was nearly dark now, the creek glittering in the last light. When his Legion had been posted up to the Wall, it was the dark that was the worst thing. After a while, it got to you. You started seeing things coming up behind. He had hated the graveyard stint on sentry go, peering out into the black night, the Picts jeering at them in their godforsaken tongue.

Hadrian may have been a great builder, but there were never enough troops to man that wall properly. By the time the Picts had raided and carried off a few sheep, the defenders were always too late. For the little dark men it was a way of life, a game. For the Legions, the punitive strikes and torching their hovels was a dispiriting chore. Those endless nights in winter quarters became a nightmare. Two of the men in the cohort had hanged themselves rather than face a third winter on the wall.

So when their tour on the frontier came to an end, they were thankful to be shot of the place and to march south for garrison duty near a fortified town called *Noviomagus,** in the territory of the *Regni*.

Marcus liked the South. A gentle country. Rome had signed treaties with the local chieftains, letting them run their own affairs, provided they were prompt in paying their tribute. In return, the local rulers could count on Roman protection against marauding neighbours.

Over the years the *Pax Romana* had worked pretty well. The countryside astride the Downs was at peace and a number of Romans had brought their families over and settled. Marcus had been amazed by the magnificence of some of their houses, nestling in the folds of the hills north of *Noviomagus* and along the coastal plain. He was not surprised when many of the time-expired Legionaries chose to stay on, marry the fair-haired Saxon girls and make their homes in that green, well-wooded land.

For the last six months of his Legion's tour in Britain, Marcus had been on detachment, mounting guard at the King's palace at Fishbourne. It was a cushy job and he had plenty of free time. When he was not on duty, he often walked down to the edge of the Harbour to watch the men building barges and fishing boats in the yard. They built the vessels in the open and launched them at high water, down wooden slipways greased with tallow. There were always several boats on the stocks, being built or repaired, having new planks fitted or a coat of pitch on the hull.

* Chichester

4

One spring morning, Marcus was standing on the saltings, watching a pair of geese foraging in the mud. It was a blustery day and a white ribbon of froth marked the edge of the incoming tide. A small rowing boat with a young boy aboard was tossing about fifty yards offshore. Marcus heard a shout and saw the dinghy lurch. The boy was leaning over the side, trying to reach an oar that was drifting off to leeward. He lost his balance and the boat capsized. Marcus saw the boy struggling in the water, trying to swim ashore. Marcus threw off his cloak, ran to the edge of the creek and plunged in. The water was freezing. He swam out to the boy and towed him ashore. Marcus wrapped the shivering lad, who seemed about ten, in his cloak and carried him up to the house of Icca, the shipwright, just behind the boatyard. The housewife fussed over them and sat Marcus and the boy before the open fire with some mulled ale. Icca came in. When he saw the boy, he gasped.

'My young Lord! Are you all right?'

'I haven't drowned, Icca, thanks to this Roman. But you may have to build me a less tippy boat.'

Icca turned to Marcus. 'I've seen you around the yard. You did a good day's work today. And the King will be grateful.'

'Why so?' asked Marcus.

'Because this is Edric, his younger son.'

When they were dry, Edric tried to give Marcus back his cloak but Marcus made him keep it. The boy shook his hand and asked his name.

Icca walked with the young Earl back to Fishbourne Palace and Marcus thanked Icca's wife for her kindness. He noticed, as he was leaving the house, that their grown-up daughter had a beautiful, serene face – and she was blind.

Next morning, his Centurion summoned Marcus. 'I'm told you've been swimming?'

'Sir.'

'The King wants to thank you. Best uniform. Two hours time. At the Palace. Be smartly turned out. Well done. Dismiss.'

Marcus was rather amused. The old man never wasted words.

Two hours later, on the dot, a slave met Marcus at the palace entrance, and escorted him through a courtyard to the King's audience chamber. It had been decorated some three centuries earlier during the reign of *Cogidubnus.** A mosaic of a sea-horse with a writhing tail spread across the centre of the tiled floor. The King and a group of his companions were warming themselves around a charcoal brazier. Marcus saluted and waited. The old soldier's maxim applied: Don't speak till you're spoken to. Anyway, he wasn't very good with kings. But this one was smiling at him.

'My son has told me what you did. I owe you two things: his life and your cloak.'

The King asked Marcus about his military service and if he would be leaving when his Legion was posted. Marcus said he wasn't sure.

'If you do decide to stay, let my reeve know. I will grant you a plot of land in payment of my debt. Meanwhile, this is a token of my thanks for saving Edric.'

A servant handed Marcus a leather satchel and, when he got outside, he undid the string and poured a stream of coins into his helmet.

In the following months, Marcus and Icca became quite friendly. The Roman occasionally gave Icca a hand in his boatyard, when one of the workmen was off sick. Icca had noticed that the soldier was skilled with his hands. One morning, when Marcus was helping shift some timber from the saw pit, an apprentice dropped a heavy oak beam on the Roman's foot. Icca

* See Note 2, page 15

6

helped him to limp up to his house and the women rubbed some herbal liniment on to the swollen ankle. Icca liked the way Marcus made a joke of the accident and refused to blame the apprentice.

'We've all had to learn the trade,' he said. And he told them about his own apprenticeship as a carpenter in Umbria.

The next evening, Icca asked Marcus into the house for a pot of mead, which the soldier was developing a taste for. His foot was still painful and he had been let off mounting the quarter guard that night. As they sat before the fire, Icca asked what Marcus planned to do when the Legion left.

'The King asked me the same question. l told him I wasn't sure. But I've been turning it over in my mind. There's nothing much for me back in Umbria. My parents are dead and my elder brother has the house. I don't know that I could settle down there now. Perhaps I've been abroad too long. I've been talking to the lads in the unit. Some have decided to stay on here. And,' he smiled at Icca and his daughter, 'the ale's not bad and the girls are pretty.'

Icca looked at the soldier, weighing him up. He wasn't a bad chap, for a Roman. More of a sense of humour than some he'd known. A strong worker, too.

'Let me know when you've made up your mind. You could have a job with me. My chippy's got so feeble in his joints he can hardly handle a saw. You could take his place. I'd be glad to have you. There's not much money in it, but you wouldn't starve.'

Marcus looked into the fire, sipping his mead.

'That's a good offer. I'll sleep on it.'

That night in his bunk, Marcus fretted. It was a big decision. The Legion was his home. He would miss it. But the barrack room scuttlebutt was that their next posting would be Libya and one of the men had served there. According to him, life on the *Limes* in the Cyrenaican desert was all mud forts and scorpions and brackish water. He wouldn't mind working with Icca. He knew he could build boats. As he dozed, he remembered the glint on the daughter's long fair hair as it fell below her shoulders, when she poured the mead slowly from the wooden jug. It would feel soft.

When he woke, Marcus had made his decision. At the next pay parade, he formally applied for an honourable discharge. The Centurion knew he was a good man and didn't want to lose him. But it was Roman policy to encourage time-expired men to settle in the Imperial frontier provinces. They made for stability, and became a reserve of manpower if trouble broke out. He had been hearing recently about foreign pirates raiding the British coast. Men like this one might come in handy. So he granted the request. Marcus signed an undertaking to return to the colours, if required; and the clerk handed him the bounty he had earned after fifteen years' good conduct, with a bonus for the wound stripe from the Ardennes.

The day before his Legion embarked in the transports that filled the Fishbourne creek, Marcus handed in his equipment to the Quartermaster. He was allowed to keep his father's old sword with the nick in the blade.

That night, the whole cohort got blind drunk. The leaving party went on till dawn, when the grey-faced troops stumbled into the barges that ferried them out to the ships anchored in the channel. Marcus watched from the shore as his friends clambered up the rope ladders hanging down the ships' sides.

Loading the men and horses and all the baggage took the whole morning. The tackle hoisting one of the horses aboard broke when it was half way up the side. The horse got tangled in the rope sling and was dragged under water by the force of the ebb.

At last the Legion was on board. The ships raised anchor. Their sweeps and the tide under them took the convoy down harbour.

Marcus waved back to his mess-mates, who were leaning over the side of the last transport to get under weigh. He watched until the ships rounded the bend of the channel below the Dell. Then he was on his own. He had made his choice and would just have to make the best of it. He threw a penny far out into the water, for luck. Perhaps somebody, one day, would find it.

★   ★   ★

The penny must have worked. As Marcus was walking back along the path from the jetty, he met one of the companions who had been with the King on the day he had been summoned to the Palace. The Briton asked Marcus what he was going to do now that his Legion had left. Marcus told him about Icca's offer of a job.

'Where will you live?'

Marcus admitted he didn't know. The horseman rode on and Marcus thought no more of their encounter. But he told Icca he would like to work for him. Next morning, his first at the yard, the King's reeve rode up and called Marcus over.

'My Lord keeps faith. I believe you need land for a house. You may have half a hide on the point between the Dell and Birdham. Come up to the palace tomorrow and you can swear fealty to the Lord. If you are willing to offer him your service and your sword, in return he will protect you and yours.'

That was how the Roman became the liegeman of a King of the *Regni,* who was himself a Legate of the Emperor. And how a former Legionary was granted a plot on the edge of the Harbour.

When Marcus came to pace out his property with the King's surveyor, he saw how generous the King had been. It was a lovely spot, facing west. It would get the afternoon sun. The channel opposite widened out to become a lake at high water. The forest came down to the water's edge on the far bank. His shoreline stretched a hundred yards either side of a shingle point where, for centuries, the Britons had dug out the red earth for the copperas which they used as a mordaunt for dying their brightly coloured cloaks. The spongy grass inland from the saltings at the water's edge was fringed with sea lavender.

Marcus planned in his mind where he would build: fifty yards inland on some firm ground. A stream with good clear water marked one side of his land. A copse of holm oak, bent with the prevailing wind, would give shelter from the south-west. If he looked northwards, he could see the run of the Downs, on whose crests the ancient tribes had built their strongholds. And it would only be a ten-minute walk to the boatyard.

That afternoon Marcus brought Icca and his family to inspect his new domain. Icca's wife remembered coming there as a child to pick blackberries and Icca showed Marcus where the fishermen used to lay their nets off the point, to catch mullet. They agreed he had been given a good deal. But, as Ella, Icca's daughter said, he deserved it.

★   ★   ★

For the next few months, Marcus worked as he had never worked before, in the morning learning his new trade as a shipwright, then, while the light lasted, building his house. He cut down a stand of oak half a mile from his land for the uprights and roof beams. Icca lent him his team of horses to drag the logs over to the site. It took him a week, plus the cost of hiring a cart, to bring back a load of cobbles for the foundations from the beach at *Cymenes Ora,** near the harbour mouth. An old man, who needed the work, showed him the local way of building wattle and daub walls and thatching the roof with reeds from the beds at the head of the creek.

The King's surveyor rode over several times to see how the work was going, usually managing to find something to criticise. Icca's family were much more encouraging. Icca made a heavy oak chest for the main room as a present. Marcus put his clothes and his father's sword in it.

At last, the day came when he could light the fire in the hearth, using driftwood from the shore. He poured a libation to his household gods. Icca's wife didn't approve of the Roman gods: hers were the natural spirits of the water and the woods. But, being a gentle creature, she kept her thoughts to herself. Marcus was a good boy, with an eye for Ella. Anyway, Icca was obviously pouring part of the libation down his own throat!

Having set himself up in his own home, Marcus concentrated on mastering the art of building boats. Many of the basic skills he needed were those he had learnt as a boy. But their application was highly specialised. Icca had an arrangement with a forester up at Dean whose team of oxen dragged the great oak trunks from the forest on the southern slope of the Downs. Then the work

* See Note 3, page 16

10

started. Each log had to be positioned with levers, so that it lay above the saw pit, chocked securely in place. Icca stood on top of the log with one end of the long double-handed saw, while Marcus stood in the pit. There was no short cut.

It was terrible work, keeping the blade straight, the sawdust sticking to the sweat on his back and gumming up his eyes. Sometimes the blade would jam against the green wood. The only way to free it was by splitting the log with a beetle and wedge. The sawing was only the beginning. The wood had to be carefully stacked so that the air circulated around the green timber until it had seasoned sufficiently to be stable. Some of the wood had to be selected to allow the grain to follow the curve of the boat's ribs or knees.

Icca took great trouble not to waste his timber and, as he said, to make the grain work for him. Each plank had to be planed and shaped by hand. Marcus watched Icca at work with an adze, his wrist loose, flicking the tool along the edge of a plank; never using a rule and never seeming to exert himself. As if nature had meant it, the plank would take on the shape Icca wanted, its line straight as a die.

Icca carried the shape of his hulls in his head. Most of his boats were built for the harbour fishermen. They knew the size they wanted. Being highly suspicious of anything new, they usually ordered the same dimensions as the craft they had crewed in for their fathers, when they were boys.

Over the years, the boats had been shaped by experience and the harsh disciplines of the sea. The boats had certain well defined tasks. They had to be rowed and set a square sail that would take them home, when wind and tide served. They had to be stable and shallow in draft, with a broad transom over which an oyster trawl or a net could be handled. They had to be strong enough to last, with deep bilge keels so the hulls could stand the battering of lying on drying moorings, or being hauled up a shingle beach. The boats needed the carrying capacity to bring home a heavy catch of fish. Above all, they had to be sea-kindly – that special quality marking the chasm between a good boat and a bad; the elusive virtue on which her crew's life could depend.

Because the fishermen, bargemen, traders and ferrymen of the Harbour knew that, for over forty years, Icca had built boats with these qualities, he was never short of work. There was only one snag. His customers had to wait. Icca was not to be hurried. It was not that he didn't work hard. He did. But he was a true Celt in the strength of his superstitions. If the omens were bad, he would have thought it folly to lay a keel. A smooth launch demanded favourable conditions. Icca had a secret spell. He cast it at night when he had the yard to himself. By the light of a full moon, he carved his own mark on the keelson. Somehow, it made him feel happier. It was his blessing.

Marcus admired the strength of Icca's boats. In shape, they were not so different from the fishing craft of the Mediterranean. But he could never quite get used to the British way of rowing an open boat, pulling the oar. In the inland sea, you pushed, standing up facing forward.

Before long, Marcus was helping to lay the planking, carvel style, on the ribs, caulking their edges with pitch and oakum. To prepare the pitch, they built a wood fire on the shingle beach, boiling up the tar in a copper cauldron until it bubbled. They plunged rags on the end of long sticks into the black liquid and smeared it over the hull to stop weed fouling the bottom and to preserve the wood.

Once the omens were right, it was time for the launch. Most of the new owners made a day of it and brought their families along. Icca's wife served ale. Icca sacrificed a cock, pouring its blood over the boat's bow. Everybody helped to slide the boat down the slipway and they cheered when she floated for the first time. They all knew she would leak a bit until the seams had taken up. But Icca was satisfied with his handiwork, glad that she looked at home on her own element, no longer land-bound, but a part of the Harbour.

By the time Marcus had built his house at Copperas point and established himself at the boatyard, the harbour community had come to accept the big Roman. He could even make himself pretty well understood in the local dialect. Ella gave him lessons in the evening after work. They both came to treasure those times together. Icca's wife welcomed their obvious fondness for each other. She would have preferred her only child to have married a Briton. Still, the Roman was a decent man and not everyone would want a blind girl as a wife.

The summer after the Legion had left, Marcus asked Icca's permission to marry his daughter. He gave a quarter of his army bounty money as a marriage bond. The priest from Apuldram joined their hands, before witnesses and all Ella's family in a ceremony which followed the ancient British rites. Although Marcus had been baptised a Christian, the Legion had remained faithful to the old gods for ceremonial occasions. It seemed to Marcus that the old British beliefs had much in common with that tradition. He was quite happy to conform to local custom. And Ella had wanted it.

After the wedding, all the guests sat around a great bonfire on the beach. Its flames reached up to the stars on that soft August night, spitting sparks from the salty driftwood. Long before the barrels of ale were empty and the bones of the sheep had been picked bare, Marcus and Ella stole away to their new home, down harbour.

The following spring, when the geese were honking northwards in their great skeins, Ella gave birth to a strong, dark boy. They called him Icca after his grandfather. By the time he was four, he was acting as his mother's eyes, and trotting along the shore path to watch his father at work in the yard. One of the fishermen taught him how to catch shrimps in a little net at low tide. It was a happy time for the family. Marcus thought it was a good life for a boy, growing up by the Harbour. Little Icca could swim when he was five; and, for his sixth birthday, Marcus built him a rowing punt with a flat bottom, eight-feet long.

But something was beginning to worry Marcus, although he kept it to himself. His corner of the Harbour was very cut off from the outside world. It took the whole day to ride in to *Noviomagus*, and he only made the journey to stock up with canvas, rope and iron fastenings for the boats.

Traders with their train of pack horses occasionally rode past and stopped at the yard to barter for fresh bass and flounders. Their gossip was disturbing. They confirmed what Marcus had already heard from the troops themselves: Rome was steadily thinning out its military presence in the Province. The Legions were increasingly needed to defend other parts of the Imperial frontier. And some of the settler families who had been in Britain for two centuries were selling their land and leaving.

It was true that much of the machinery of Roman administration remained in place but every day there were signs that the old civic order was gradually breaking down: city walls left unrepaired; fields left untilled; taxes not collected; law-breaking; a decline in the cross-Channel trade.

Cogidubnus's successors had failed to impose their authority, and the local chieftains were quarrelling among themselves. Some of the magnates promoted by Rome were weakening in their allegiance and beginning to stake out territorial claims and to arm their followers, if only in self protection. Travellers' tales suggested that this pattern was being repeated in other provinces of the Empire.

What worried Marcus even more were the rumours he was hearing about pirates from across the North Sea raiding the coastal settlements. One day, a tinker reported that some pirate ships had even wintered in a creek on the northern side of the island the Romans called *Vectis*.*

One misty morning, as the flood tide was creeping over the saltings, Marcus was shaping a pair of oars for an oyster punt on the foreshore in front of his house. It was a still day with no wind. He heard the noise a long way off: the slap and thud of an oared vessel rowing up the harbour with the tide. Looking down channel, he saw the prow of a ship coming out of the mist. She was much narrower and longer than the local craft. As the

* Isle of Wight

stranger came closer, a shaft of sunlight glinted on a metal helmet as the lookout pointed towards his house.

Marcus ran up the path, grabbing young Icca on the way. Ella was baking bread in the oven behind the kitchen. By the time Marcus had bundled them both inside, the ship's bow with its dragon figurehead had scrunched on the shingle of the point, and her crew were leaping over the side and wading ashore. They rushed up the path, screaming and waving double-handed axes. Marcus took down his father's sword from its rack above the fireplace and stood behind the door. Ella was hugging Icca when the door burst open. A bearded man with long fair hair stood there, yelling, axe in hand. Marcus rushed at him out of the darkness and drove the point of his sword through his enemy's neck. Four more pirates charged through the door, axes flailing. Ella never saw her husband die, facing his front, as the Legion had taught him, taking two more of the attackers with him. Nor did she see the axe as it swung down on her head.

Icca watched both his parents die. He did not scream. He grabbed a broom and stood in the corner over his mother, sobbing as he stabbed at the nearest giant devil with all his seven-year-old strength. The giant laughed and swept the broom handle aside. He picked up the boy and carried him, kicking, back to the ship. A brave lad. He might make a useful seaman.

NOTES

1   **The Roman Coin**

Some years later, when he was at university John consulted the Director of the Roman Palace at Fishbourne about the coin with the worn head on one side and galley on the reverse. After some research, he was able to identify the coin as a bronze 'quinarius' of the Emperor Allectus. He became Emperor on A.D.293 and was killed in battle in A.D.296. The letters CL along the bottom suggest that the coin was probably minted at Clausentum, modern day Bitterne, near Southampton. This is interesting, as the Roman Road from Chichester to Bitterne ran among the northern edge of Chichester Harbour and Bosham Creek, where John was shrimping.

2   **Togidubnus**

The latest research has concluded the first letter of his name should be T not C. Tiberius Claudius Togidubnus was a 1st-century A.D. King who ruled a tribe called the Regni, which was centred in Chichester. It is believed that he was installed by the Romans as a Client King to look after Rome's interests in the area, which he seems to have done successfully. At the time of the Boudiccan Revolt in A.D.43, when British tribes sacked Colchester, St Albans and London, there appears to have been no unrest in this area. In gratitude, the Emperor Vespasian may well have had the magnificent Palace at Fishbourne built for him. It was built on the same site as the military supply base that was set up at the time of the Claudian invasion in A.D.43. A navigable channel ran up from the Harbour almost to the Palace itself, but probably fell out of use in the late 3rd century A.D. From Elizabethan times up to the early 19th century, Dell Quay was Chichester's principal port.

3   **Cymenes Ora**

Cymenes Ora, the shore of Cymen, was recorded as the landing place in Britain in A.D.457 of the Saxon Chieftain, Aella. The exact site is uncertain, but one possibility is thought to lie somewhere between Pagham and Chichester Harbour. Cymen was one of Aella's sons. Aella's name is preserved by Ella Nore, the small headland just to the east of East Head, down by the harbour entrance. Who knows? Aella may actually have landed there!

Interlude

THE TIDE

The rhythm of the tide gives the Harbour its life.

For seven hours, the salt water floods in from the open sea in the eastern approaches to the Solent, across the sand bar, half a mile south of the narrow entrance between the Pole Sand to the west and the Winner shoal to eastward. At the harbour mouth, the Hayling Island shingle drops off sharply to sixty feet of water – much the deepest part of the Harbour. The surface of the water here is never at rest while the tide is running, swirling with miniature whirlpools, riffled by overfalls. Down below, contrary eddies stir up the bottom into a broth, laced with crabs and shellfish and worms which the cod fatten on in winter. In summer, the school bass feed on the fry in the troubled upper water, like sheep dogs rounding up a silvery flock. In July, when the shoals of mackerel come foraging over the bar, the surface is fretted into a white frenzy as the packs of predators hunt the whitebait, and terns dive for their share of the feast.

To a sea bird, flying overhead, the Harbour looks like a man's hand, its fingers outstretched. The entrance, at the narrow wrist, opens up to the broad basin of the palm of the hand, while the five principal channels stretch inland. The two smaller western channels, Mengham and Mill Rythe, form the joint and tip of the thumb. The four outstretched fingers are the longer channels leading northwards up to Emsworth, Thorney, Bosham and the most easterly and longest of all the channels, winding past Itchenor, Birdham and Dell Quay up to Fishbourne. As the bird flies north, the fingers narrow at their tips and small streams, some of them only winter bournes, meander across the coastal plain, bringing fresh water to mingle with the salt at the heads of the creeks. These gliding streams rise from cool aquifers deep in the chalk on the southern slopes of the Downs. All the land surrounding the Harbour is so well watered and fertile, and so favoured by sunshine, that its bounty spills over into the Harbour itself, nourishing its weed, sediment and the salt-loving grasses on the shoreline; giving rich feeding grounds, above and below water, to the harbour wildlife.

At high tide, the palm of the hand, where all the fingers meet, becomes a great inland sea, whose shores flicker in summer in the mirage of noon. In winter, when a gale whips across from the south-west against the ebb, the fetch of the waves builds up until it crashes against the lee shores and undermines the sea defences. In the gales, the sea foam is thrown against the holm oaks, decorating their spindly branches, and all the stunted shoreline trees grow bent with the force of that prevailing wind. Tidewrack fringes the high water mark; driftwood, cuttlefish and tangled netting turn grey in the sun. A crust of decaying seaweed, where sea lice and tiny crabs scavenge, marks the tide line and combines with mud and salt to give the Harbour its distinctive smell.

At high tide, when the Harbour is brim full, the water sleeps for about half an hour, if the wind lets it. The saltings and the mud flats are covered; water laps against the grassy sea walls and tree roots. At the highest spring tides, and when the water level is swollen by an onshore gale, the sea threatens to burst its banks and flood across the surrounding countryside.

The Harbour is not easily confined.

Nor does the stand of high water last for long. Starting at the edges of the channels, the old rhythm begins all over again. The tide turns, gently at first, and slowly gathers its strength. The ebb flows much faster than the flood. At the mouth, where it runs at its strongest, the tide races out at about 5 knots, emptying and cleansing the Harbour every twelve hours. The ebb flushes detritus and effluent out to sea with an enormous amount of sediment, scouring the mud from the channels and altering the shape of the Harbour with every tide. As the ebb takes away, so the flood brings back, depositing the mud particles at the top of the creeks. The force of the tide and waves together keeps the Harbour in perpetual motion, shifting the sand banks, washing away shingle beaches and digging out new channels. Each autumn gale creates new contours. Down at the mouth, the sand dunes are eroded by the force of wind and wave, threatening to breach the Hinge at East Head – that guardian of the Harbour's character.

As the tide drops, the saltings begin to show; curlew, dunlin and oystercatchers investigate the food buried in the emerging mud. A myriad of tiny organisms work the water's edge. Lug worms leave the spirals of their tell-tale casts in the wet sand; where the gravel mingles with the mud, the rag worms nip their food with powerful pincers.

By low water, the Harbour has shrunk to a skeleton. The inland sea of the lower harbour has become a wide river, guarded by sand banks. The channels draining down to it have all narrowed; the heads of the creeks have shrunk to a trickle.

Mud is king. Soft, squelching, sticky, slimy, smelly, glutinous mud. Dull grey when the low clouds scud overhead. Glistening silver in the sunshine. Polished by the tide and rounded like a well-sucked jujube. Mud gives the upper harbour its quality and its life.

The grasses and the plants that tolerate salt water link the mud to the dry land. Some store the water they need in their bodies to prevent a salty dehydration; others dig their roots deep down until they find moisture. The blanket weeds thrive on the fertilisers washed off the land. The spartina grass, whose roots hold together the edges of the little channels, comes and goes with a mysterious cycle of its own. Where the saltings reach up to the high water mark, the plants of the sea shore spread their yellow and purple blossoms.

If the lower harbour is a seascape, washed by horizontal planes of white and blue and grey, higher up, the Harbour is transformed into a landscape of rivers, winding through woods and fields. This is the inland world of Gainsborough and the Norwich school, not of Boudin and Dufy on the beach. Even the colour of the water is different, often taking on a greenish tint, in imitation of the gorse and oak and tamarisk lining the banks.

The Sussex light is as restless as the tide. There are days, usually in winter, when the bleak sunlight slanting through the chasing clouds turns the surface to a cold steel blue, as bitter as the So'Wester itself.

Chapter II

VIKING

Old Lob didn't think much of these Danes. A snooty bunch of outlandish thugs. They hadn't been over here more than a couple of tides and here they were, screwing money out of God-fearing Christians baptised by Wilfrid himself – a tax they called *Wergild*. More like blackmail, that's what it really was. All to pay for their fleet and the housecarls. They thought they could take over the place. Laying down the law so a man could hardly breathe without being fined. Mind you, that there King who called himself Cnut did like his place here at Bosham. Kept some of his ships in the channel, so he must have a drop of sense.

Old Lob knew one thing for sure. Cnut might be a powerful lord. But he had a lot to learn about the Harbour. Lob had to laugh: why, the man had even tried to master the sea. Lob had watched the whole thing from his punt. What a carry on!

It had all started when the King had sent his men to dig a dyke across the top of the channel to the west of the church, the church where Cnut's daughter lay buried, poor lass. (A pretty little thing – one day Old Lob had ferried her and her nurse across the creek so she could have a closer look at the geese on the other side.)

Anyway, they'd shovelled cartloads of earth and shingle to build the dam. Some daft foreign idea about turning the head of the creek into a lagoon where the baby oysters could grow fat. Cnut had come over with his fancy thegns to tell the workmen what to do.

'More stones, more stones!'

In the end, Cnut's dyke got built and the King went off to do his ruling. And what happened? The first winter gale blew a great hole in the wall, as Lob always said it would. Stood to reason, didn't it? The old sea came surging in. Washed the whole lot away by the next spring tide. Lob had to laugh. Cnut thought he could tame the Harbour, did he? Got his feet wet, and no mistake.

★   ★   ★

Old Lob was a Man of Bosham. Like his father and grandfather before him, he guarded that designation jealously. Since time out of mind, the men of Bosham had enjoyed special privileges, valuable ones. They were exempt from paying dues to the lord and were free to fish throughout the Harbour and to use the quay at Bosham without payment of tolls. Only men who were the sons of Men of Bosham, and who made their living from the sea, were admitted to the fellowship.

Nobody could remember when they first started calling Lob 'Old'. He was over seventy now. He had never learnt to read or write. He had never needed to. He was a fisherman, and what he needed to know was how to set a net across the tide, where the deep holes were in the channels where the flatfish congregated, and the secrets of calling the mallard into his traps. These things he knew better than anyone else in Bosham.

He lived by himself in a thatched hut on the edge of the creek, mooring his flat-bottomed punt to a stake on the foreshore. Whenever the tide served, he set his nets and laid his night lines. In those days the Harbour teemed with fish. The Lord's steward came down to the quay and took most of his sea trout, which he caught on their way up to the mill stream to spawn. The Lord was also partial to a fine bass and to the eels which Lob smoked himself.

That summer, the steward had told him, the Norsemen were raiding England. Cnut had fitted out his fleet earlier in the season, and had sent his Bosham squadron to the Isle of Wight to guard the approaches to the Solent. The coastguards had reported a number of Viking ships off Pevensey, making their way westward, pillaging as they went.

One July morning, Lob had just come in from a night's fishing when he saw a strange ship alongside the quay. From the other side of the creek, he heard a great battering coming from the direction of the church. Nobody seemed to be around in the village. That was unusual. He didn't like it. As a precaution, Lob hid in the reeds and peeped out. Then he saw the dragon head on the prow of the ship. She was a Norseman.

The villagers must have had warning, carried up harbour from the watch tower on East Head, and fled inland. How had the Viking got past Cnut's ships? Nothing he could do.

Lob had been crouching in the reeds for about an hour when he saw the ship's crew. They were staggering back to the quay, roaring with laughter, carrying the church bell slung between two long poles.

Lob watched as the Norsemen levered the great bell on board and lashed it athwartship on planks. The tide was ebbing now. The wind had got up. Lob guessed they were in a hurry to be off. They would have taken what they could carry from the church. There wasn't much else worth having nearby, and they wouldn't want to miss the tide. The steersman let her bows swing round until the long ship faced down stream. The crew unshipped their oars and began to pull, wind against the ebb.

Old Lob ran along the path on the east side of the channel, keeping out of sight. The Viking was off Cobnor near the mouth of the Bosham channel when the squall hit her. By the time she had reached the main channel at Deep End, it was blowing hard. The vessel was feeling the full force of the So'Wester. She was listing heavily to port; starting to ship water. Lob saw one of the crew lose his hand hold and slip overboard to leeward. The ship was nearly on her beam ends, out of control. She was obviously top heavy with the great bell so high above the waterline. The crew had their axes out to slash the rope lashings. The bell slid down the planks into the water. The ship righted herself and her oarsmen took her down harbour.

The man who had fallen overboard was swimming slowly towards the shore. Lob ran to the point just below where the exhausted seaman was drifting past. He waded into the water and grabbed the man's collar. He was very heavy, but Lob managed to drag him to the bank and turn him over on his back. The Norseman, covered in mud, was half choked with seawater. But he opened his eyes and stared at the Englishman. He wondered whether to kill the old man. As he had probably saved his life, he decided not to. He sat up and was sick. He wiped his mouth with a sodden sleeve. The old man helped him to his feet.

'My name's Icca,' the Viking said. But Lob didn't understand his speech. Anyway he wasn't concentrating on the half-drowned stranger. He was listening. Between the gusts of wind, Old Lob was almost sure he heard the Bosham church bell toll.

Icca looked down the Harbour and saw his ship far off. No hope of catching her. He was on his own and his teeth were chattering. He could hardly walk. He let the old man lead him back to the village. When they were among the cottages by the waterside, a small crowd gathered, pointing at him. They had hidden from the pirates who had robbed their church. Had Lob heard the news? And who was this bedraggled stranger?

Old Lob made the most of his story and the Saxons turned on the Viking. So he was one of the villains who had walked off with their bell! Well, they'd string him up and strike *him* till he rang. One of the old women who cleaned the church went up to Icca and spat in his face. Two of the men seized and bound his arms behind him. A stone hit his nose and it started to bleed. It was the last straw. Icca had reached that Norse stage of not caring a toss whether he lived or died. A kind of madness filled him and he roared his defiance.

'You miserable, dung-eating cowherds. Go on, kill me, you turds. But let me die with a sword in my hand and, by Thor, I'll show you mud creepers how a Viking behaves!'

One of the Lord's thegns had been sitting on his horse at the edge of the crowd. He not only heard the Viking but understood what he said. Both the thegn and his master, like King Cnut, were Danes and the Danish tongue and the stranger's were not so different. The outlaw was plainly a man of spirit; and the thegn had to admit that only a few years ago the Danes themselves were plundering the Saxon shore in the same ruthless way as these Norsemen. His Earl might be glad to have the fellow hold an oar in his ship. The King's fleet was short-handed, as usual. It looked like being a busy summer, with all the reports of the Norsemen going a-viking around the British coasts. Cnut was going to need every trained seaman he could find. If this lad had sailed down from Norway, he must know one end of a rope from the other. The thegn rode into the group of excited villagers.

'Unbind this man,' he ordered. 'My Master will want to question him.' Swearing under their breath, they did as they were told and Icca rubbed his wrists.

Speaking in Danish, the thegn made Icca run beside his horse as he trotted towards the Earl's house near the top of the creek. When they arrived, Icca was led to an outhouse. The door was barred. A tough-looking servant brought him dry clothes and some stew in a wooden bowl. He spent a cold night on the dirt floor.

The following morning, he was brought into a long hall with straw-strewn paving stones. Heavy wooden beams supported a thatched roof; an open hearth smouldered at the far end. Two long tables with benches lined either side.

A thin-faced man was sitting by the fire, stroking a wolf-hound. The dog got up and showed his fangs as Icca approached. Two men in chain mail, holding spears at the ready, stood nearby. The thegn who had rescued Icca presented him.

'This is the Norseman I told you about, my Lord.'

The Earl examined Icca for a minute. Icca returned the stare. He saw a man of about forty, wearing a short, stabbing sword. A wiry, active man, used to command, with a weather-beaten face, perhaps a seaman, almost certainly a soldier. One of the King's companions.

The Earl spoke in Danish to Icca, and asked him about his ship and his voyage and how he had come to raid Bosham. He was particularly interested to learn where Icca had come from, who was his leader and whether he had sailed in a fleet. Icca thought it best to give a fairly full account of his voyage from Norway, being careful not to reveal the true number of ships in company with his own.

While Icca told his story, the Earl studied his face. He was mostly telling the truth, but he was giving nothing away about his companions in the other ships of the Norse fleet. The Earl approved. He did not like treacherous men, and this man had no doubt sworn to follow his captain faithfully. Cnut was having quite enough trouble with turncoats. The Earl motioned to a servant to hand the Norseman a beaker of mead.

'My name is Thorveig. I command King Cnut's ships in these waters. You and your crew were lucky that I was over on the Isle of Wight when you came a-viking to the Harbour. Otherwise, it would have been the worse for you.'

Thorveig asked about the bell and where his vessel was bound. Icca told how the bell had been lost overboard. Thorveig laughed when his thegn reported that the story was going the rounds of Bosham that the old fisherman, Lob, who had pulled the Viking out of the water, swore he had heard the bell tolling under water.

'Perhaps it was your death knell, Norseman,' Thorveig remarked. 'Tell me your name.'

'I am Icca.'

'That name seems to me more Saxon than Norse.'

'You are right. My father, Ulf, used to say that many of my family had borne the name. According to our family saga, in olden times an ancestor had come across to Norway as a boy when he had been captured in a raid on this island. I can tell you no more than that. As for where my ship is heading, I truly do not know. And if I did, it would be shameful to betray my shipmates. We were cruising along the coast and the captain had not decided whether to spend the winter season on the Saxon shore. My own opinion is that it would have been best to sail home before the autumn gales.'

Thorveig thought well of this speech. It suggested both loyalty and seamanship.

'Icca, now that you have emptied your beaker, listen with care to what I have to say. I have saved your life. So you owe me a debt. You have done serious injury to Bosham and there is no doubt that, under Cnut's law, you should be condemned to die. Neither, before you were killed, would you be given back your sword, nor could you expect to be buried with respect, your weapon at your side. These are considerations that touch your honour. You must weigh them. Equally, your shipmates have abandoned you, so you are released from your duty to them. From your own account, it would seem that you are now back in the land of your ancestors.

'For all these reasons, the balance of your interest would now be served by swearing loyalty to me and becoming my man. Not only will I spare your life. I will give you an honoured place aboard one of my ships. I already have several of your countrymen among the crews.'

Icca considered that Thorveig's words were fair. He told the Earl that he was ready to become his man and he took his hand as witness to his bond. Thorveig made Icca sit down and tell him more about his time at sea.

Icca told his story simply but Thorveig and his thegn were also seamen. They understood what he was talking about. The drink had loosened Icca's tongue. When he spoke of his days at sea, he was almost crooning, as if he was telling one of the sagas he remembered his grandfather telling by the fireside during the winter nights when he was a boy.

'As for my seamanship, let the first gale try me! The sea is all I have known. My family were farmers on good land at the head of a fjord south of Trondheim. I was the younger son and when my parents died, the farm went to my elder brother and there was no room for me. I was sixteen and ready for the sea. Our neighbour, Sigur, a well-known captain, agreed to take me with him. At that time, he was trading up the Russian rivers. When the ice melted, we rowed for days against the current, until our hands bled and we slept over our oars. We beached our long ship at night, lighting fires on the bank to keep the wolves away.

'Sigur knew that the higher up the rivers we could row, the higher the profit we could make on the furs and slaves we bartered for in the summer fairs. Those were great occasions. The Russians came from hundreds of miles on their ponies and sledges, driving their horses and cattle with them. They set up their tents beside the river, with stalls selling everything from cheese to their women (who often smelt worse than the cheese!).

'Sigur knew that he had to let his crew get drunk when we reached a new fairground. So we usually spent a week at each of the fairs, before paddling upstream. In the upper reaches, we had to pull the ship on rollers to get above the rapids. That was the hardest work of all. That, and swatting the black flies that drove us mad at the end of the summer. Our freeboard got lower and lower as we stowed our cargo, so that when we sailed home down the Baltic, we had to rig hides along the lee thole pins to stop shipping water. It was the voyage home, when we were laden, that was the most dangerous time. The Swedes kept watch. It was best to pass through the Sound at night, keeping a sharp look-out.

'We traded in the northern waters for five seasons. The Russian pickings became scarcer, with too many ships spoiling the market, so we decided to try our luck at viking further south. One of the Trondheim ships had spent the winter at the mouth of one of the rivers in Gaul which never froze over, on an island called Noirmoutier. There was even talk of making a permanent camp. We landed there last November. It was a good place, with good wine. That was Sigur's bad luck: he got into a fight with a drunken priest who struck him on the back of his neck with a crucifix. The wound went bad and he died. We killed the priest to avenge Sigur and sailed in a hurry. The whole crew vowed we would have nothing more to do with the Christian god.

'I was chosen as steersman, although I was not the oldest man on board. The mate and the boatswain had fought over a woman on the island. Each refused to serve under the other. That's how I got the job. The mate was a bully and tried to bully me. So I suggested that, as changes were being made, we should throw him overboard and let him swim back to his woman. The crew talked this over and agreed. The boatswain became mate and he never gave me trouble.

'You know the rest, Thorveig. We spent this season raiding along the south coast. If I hadn't lost my footing when the ship was overburdened by that damned bell, I'd be raiding now, instead of becoming your man. But, as my fate has turned in this direction, I shall have to make the best of it.'

Thorveig congratulated Icca on his story, particularly, on the way he had disposed of the mate. Bullies often came to a bad end at sea, in his experience. He told Icca that he would soon be at sea again. He was glad to have him as one of his own followers. But he warned him, as he filled up his mug, that Icca would find him a hard man to throw overboard. Icca thought that was probably true.

While Icca was telling his story, he had not noticed Thorveig's minstrel, sitting in a dark corner of the hall. When Icca left, the minstrel began to turn over in his mind a fine new rune to sing to his master at supper, all about a slave girl up a Russian river and a magical bell that sang under the sea.*

Thorveig's prophecy was fulfilled two days later, when seven ships of his flotilla rowed up to their anchorage off Bosham quay. The crews were surly because they had failed to make contact with the Norse ships threatening the Isle of Wight. Icca was rowed out in a dinghy to Thorveig's own ship, which was two men short. She was slightly broader in the beam than Icca's old long ship, although her rig and gear were much the same: a loose-footed square sail

---

* Later on, the minstrel added a new verse to the rune: a soothsayer advised the Earl that he could haul the bell from the bottom of the channel with a team of pure-white oxen. But they had to be entirely white if the magic was to work. A team of oxen was yoked and a warp tied to the bell at dead low water. The oxen pulled. But the warp snapped. And when the oxen were unyoked, one of the animals was found to have on its neck a single black hair.

on a heavy pine mast. Twelve oars a side, with a long steering oar on the starboard quarter. Bow and stern both swept up to a carved head, which Icca later learnt was of Thorveig's favourite hound. Heavy, round boulders served as ballast in the bilges.

The vessel carried enough water and ale in barrels for a month at sea. Cheese, dried bread and salted beef made up the rations. If the sea was calm, they could boil water over a fire lit on a flat stone amidships. Her full complement was thirty and they slept in their boat cloaks on the rowing thwarts. In foul weather, they slung a tarpaulin across the hull for shelter. Whenever they could, they made camp ashore for the night, and took what food they could find in the neighbourhood.

The thegn introduced Icca to the steersman, and he showed him his rowing position, number three on bow side. Icca took this as a good omen, because that was where he had rowed when he joined Sigur. The steersman gave him the belongings of one of the men he was replacing: a heavy double-edged sword, a dagger, a metal helmet and a thick leather jerkin.

The crew were a mixed bunch, only recently joined. Three were Norsemen and they all managed to understand each other in a seaman's *lingua franca*. One man never spoke. They said the Moors had cut out his tongue when he was serving on the galleys in North Africa. Two Irishmen, inseparable, crooned together in a Celtic brogue. Three Shetland Island whale men, fine seamen forcibly taken off their whale boat, spoke among themselves in a soft tongue that sounded halfway between Norwegian and the language of the Picts. The crew were paid in gold, with double pay for sea time. They told Icca that Thorveig was a wise commander, as well as a lucky one.

The role of the Bosham flotilla that August was to guard the eastern approaches to the Solent, between Selsey Bill and the Island. As commander of the inshore squadron of Cnut's fleet, Thorveig had to work closely with the fyrd, the armed bands that the shire reeves called out when invasion threatened. A chain of watch towers looked out from all the headlands along the coast; and a system of signal fires, which Icca admired, gave early warning of the approach of the enemy.

Once the crews had filled the water casks from the mill stream, Thorveig took his ships out to sea. They rowed through the entrance. Hayling Bay was flat calm. Seagulls were resting on the tide, waiting for mackerel to chase the whitebait up to the surface. The outline of the Isle of Wight stretched mistily across the horizon.

That night, they anchored under the lee of Brading. Cnut came alongside in his barge to give Thorveig his orders.

There were twenty-three ships in the combined fleet, from Weymouth, Wareham, Southampton and even from the Thames. Three days earlier, a merchantman with a cargo of hides from Denmark had reported sighting a Viking fleet at anchor off Rye. There was little doubt they were heading west along the coast. Cnut would fight them at the mouth of the Solent. But he was careful to seek the views of his captains. They all agreed that they should use the prevailing wind while it favoured them, swooping down on the Norsemen from windward; grappling and fighting them, ship to ship. The Danish merchantman had sighted 'about two dozen' of the enemy, so it would be a fair fight. All they had to do now was watch and wait.

The story of how Icca's old ship had lost the Bosham bell had gone round the fleet. Icca was getting bored with sailors from the other ships making signs and shouting 'ding-dong!' when they saw him.

One evening, one of Cnut's pages rowed over to Icca's ship and summoned him to join Thorveig aboard the royal flagship. The King was talking to his captains in the stern, and Icca was made to tell his story all over again. When they had stopped laughing, Cnut gave Icca some wine and told him not to fall overboard again. Icca said that he would do his best. But, he added, before long, the decks of the King's ships were likely to be slippery with blood and it wouldn't be his own blood, either! Later, Thorveig told Cnut how Icca had defied the men of Bosham. They agreed he was a proud man, somebody to watch. The King also advised Thorveig to dredge the channel for the bell: it was valuable.

When Icca stretched out on his thwart that night, he thought about his meeting with Cnut. He didn't much like the way he had been treated over that bell. That was why he had spoken up rather rudely for a former enemy who had only just become one of Cnut's men. He would show the Danes when it came to fighting. And he liked the look of the King, who had the knack of making men do what they didn't want to do. In his heart, Icca didn't want to fight his countrymen. But they had left him in the lurch, and he had sworn to keep faith with Thorveig. So he would fight.

They spent a week patrolling between Bembridge and Selsey Bill, two ships on guard within sight of the body of the fleet. In good visibility, a lookout at each mast head could sight a ship about seven miles off. That meant Cnut could be alerted to an enemy presence fourteen miles away. On the seventh morning, another calm day, Thorveig's was guardship. The tongueless sailor was up the mast. Suddenly, as the crew were resting on their oars, he pointed to the east. Thorveig climbed the rigging. Nothing. The lookout grabbed his sleeves, pointing out into the Channel. There they were, a chain of tiny black dots on the sharp dividing line between sea and sky. There was no doubt. The Vikings!

They hoisted the signal. Cnut's ships raised anchor and rowed out to join the guardships. They took station, fifty yards between each vessel, bows facing east. Dark shadows swept over the surface as the sea breeze filled in. Cnut ordered the fleet to ship oars and make sail. They bore down on the enemy. Icca counted twenty long ships, all rowing steadily into the wind, their blades winking in the sun. Cnut took the centre of the line, with Thorveig on his right. The men drew their weapons from the rack by the mast and unhooked their painted shields from the coamings. They steered for the middle of the Viking fleet, their wakes cutting white furrows astern. The waiting was nearly over. The breeze freshened and Icca listened to the old sea song as the hull creamed through the water. Only about a hundred yards now, and he could hear the Vikings yelling.

They were always the same, those last seconds. A timeless blur, over in a flash. In that flash, they struck. Their prow swept along the side of the leading Viking, shearing off the looms of five of her bow side oars and catapulting their oarsmen into the gap before the two hulls crashed together. Two grapnels caught in the Norseman's shrouds and Thorveig's men made fast the lines, lashing the boats alongside. Icca landed on the enemy's coaming. One of the Shetlanders tripped and fell between the grinding hulls. Two others were hacked down as they scrambled over the side. Thorveig and Icca, followed by the rest of the crew, worked their way aft to where the Vikings had put up their shields in a defensive wall. Two of the Norsemen in Thorveig's crew, brothers from Stavanger, normally quiet men who did their duty without fuss, went berserk and rushed at the shields, screaming. They died on the points of the Viking swords. But their crazy attack had burst a gap in the shield ring, giving Thorveig and Icca space to use their swords, double-handed, scything in arcs. That was when Thorveig slipped on a bloody thwart and fell at the feet of the Norse captain. Icca stood over him, straddling his captain's body, legs wide apart. As the Norseman raised his axe, Icca sliced across his face and the man fell backwards into the bilges. The Norsemen saw their captain fall and huddled together at the stern. In fact, they were too close together to be able to fight effectively. As if a collective shudder had passed through them, they lost the will to do more, and it was all over. Some jumped over the side; the wounded were thrown overboard. Three men who asked for mercy were put to the sword.

Only then did Icca have time to see how the rest of the fleet was doing. Most of the ships had paired off to fight their private battles. Three of the enemy long boats, which had been stove in, were lying waterlogged. Six had managed to disengage and were running fast downwind. It looked as though Cnut's men had overcome most of the others.

Nearby, however, Cnut seemed to be in trouble.

His flagship was wedged between two of the Viking ships, both of whose crews were boarding her. The sea had got up and the three masts were fouling each other as the hulls rolled in the swell. It was hard enough to stand on deck, let along fight. Thorveig brought his vessel alongside the nearer Viking. His crew raced across her empty deck, swarming over her side on to the King's ship. Cnut and his housecarls had formed a ring amidships, greatly outnumbered. Thorveig's crew had surprise on their side. They fell on the Vikings from behind. It was a time for killing.

Icca had the battle madness. A stillness came over him in the middle of the slaughter. As if in a dream, he saw visions of faces, split in two; a hand, severed at the wrist, still gripping a sword; a Norseman pinned to a thwart by a broadsword through his chest. Then it was over. The madness passed. Icca found himself panting, blood oozing from his left arm. The Vikings left standing had thrown down their arms, awaiting their doom. Cnut spared their lives when he saw the extent of his victory.

Only eight of the enemy ships had escaped; the rest had either sunk or had been captured. Of Cnut's fleet, three were lost. Nearly a quarter of his men were dead or wounded. They were all dog tired. By the time they had secured the prisoners and cleared the debris of battle from their decks, it was late afternoon and the wind was dying. They had drifted far to leeward during the sea fight. It was a weary haul back to the anchorage off Brading.

In the morning, Cnut called all his captains over to the flagship and thanked them. He singled out Thorveig and his men for the way they had come to his aid. Thorveig told Cnut how Icca had saved his life. The King reminded him that he had said Icca was a man to watch. When he got back on board his own ship, Thorveig appointed Icca as his new steersman. The crew thought this choice a just one, as Icca had behaved well in battle and Thorveig owed him his life. Icca simply said that he was only being given back his former rank, but he was secretly proud as he renewed the leather lashing that bound his steering oar to its thole pin.

That evening, Cnut's men drew their long ships up on the beach at the mouth of Bembridge Haven. The islanders brought them oxen and ale for a feast. Cnut's minstrel sang the saga of the battle while the islanders listened, and the crews fell asleep on the sand under the stars.

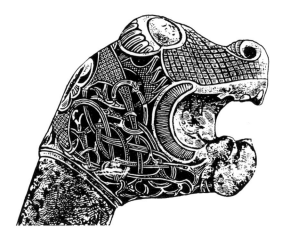

THE BASS

Instinct, and perhaps a kind of memory, led the bass home to the Harbour. He had been born there in June, in the nursery at the entrance. One egg among hundreds of thousands, floating free in the salt water, drifting up and down with the ebb and flow of the tide, at the mercy of the current and the predators. The egg was soft and opaque, not much more than a millimetre in diameter – rich food for almost every living thing bigger than itself. Its only defences were the safety that lies in numbers, and sheer chance. Chance decided if a gale would strand the egg, high and dry, on the Hayling Island shingle, to rot in the sea wind or to be nibbled by scavengers. Chance might clog the egg in a patch of diesel oil spilt by a careless motor boat. Only a tiny proportion of the eggs survived. Theirs was no Darwinian survival of the fittest, but survival dictated by chance alone.

The nutrients in the Harbour, and the light filtering through its water, suited the tiny floating balls. Larvae hatched out in a week, wide-eyed, quivering. The fingerlings gathered in silver clouds, flashing in unison, as they fed on minute organisms that enriched the water. The bass fry grew rapidly, exploring the Harbour in their schools, congregating in the disturbed water where the channels meet, chasing the whitebait near the surface and probing the muddy shallows for worms. Even when young, the bass were cannibals. They ate each other; other fish ate them.

By July, the schools of mackerel were coming into the Harbour, crossing the bar at high water, hoovering up the fry. That was a time of frenzy. The mackerel herded the little bass into a seething mass of panic, thrashing the surface of the water, while terns hovered and dived into the school, screaming. And, most sinister of all, the green-boned garfish with their long snouts, hung stationary in the upper water, their thin bodies pointing, lying in wait. Only the strongest of the bass lived long enough to swim out to sea with their parents when winter came. Or the luckiest.

After several summers of fattening in the open sea, our bass had grown to weigh six pounds. A tall dorsal fin stood high above his back, protected by nine wicked spines; his flanks were encased in a silver armour of overlapping scales. When the sunlight slanted down on him in mid water, the scales sparkled like the facets of a diamond. But from a bird's eye view, directly overhead, he was nearly invisible: the grey greeny-blue of his back blended into the surrounding water. He had remarkable staying power. He could swim steadily all day long with an effortless superiority of movement. When attacking his prey or escaping from danger, he could summon up short bursts of terrifying speed, helped by a covering film of mucus that reduced the surface tension of his body to a minimum. Nature had designed him to be an efficient killing machine.

Why did the bass return to the Harbour? Who knows? Some inherent genetic memory, the taste and smell of the water, the urge to spawn, herd instinct and the movement of his food supply may all have played their part. He needed some trigger before he swam inshore. He lay motionless in about six feet of water, near the bottom, on the seaward side of the Bar.

It was low water of a spring tide. A flat calm, the surface looking as though it had been polished. Specks of sand and weed hung in the water; the sunlight shafted down on to the sand. The sea bed was corrugated by a miniature desert of sand dunes, running in parallel lines, where the bottom had been rumpled by wave and tide. The gulls slept, one eye half-cocked, waiting for the renewal of life that would come with the beginning of the flood.

The sea almost sighed as the tide turned. A whisper of breeze, darkening the surface from the direction of the Nab Tower, gently ruffled the feathers of the floating gulls. Along his lateral line and in his gills, the bass sensed a change. He let himself drift with the current over the Bar. To his right, the sea crept across the dry sand on the Winner, melting the lug worm casts. The tide swung the strands of seaweed inland towards the Wittering beach.

The tide's edge was the hunting ground of the shrimps; flicking, feelers searching, half-buried in the sand. The bass could hear them under water, chirping like crickets as they clicked their legs together. The crabs came after them, scuttling sideways, pincers at the ready. Most of these tide runners moved surprisingly fast. Others laid traps, like the baby dabs and flounders. They lay flat, invisible against the sand, and let their food come to them.

The big bass let the incoming tide carry him through the entrance. He paused for a time in the hole on the north-west edge of the Winner, where the tide poured over the top of the sand bank, creating a back eddy that trapped a mixture of food. At full flood, he moved slowly up the Harbour, past East Head where the sand gave way to mud; past Ellanore and Chalkdock and on to Deep End, where the two channels meet. The bass was feeding on whatever he could find. On this tide, the pickings were poor. Deep End and its disturbed water was a favourite feeding ground. The fry scattered as he swam up to the Deep End mark. It was there that our bass saw and smelt the rag worm, hanging in the tide. He was still hungry and he was tempted.

38

Chapter III

NORMAN

Engeler was a Norman clerk who had come over to England ten years after Duke William's invasion. His parents had died of the fever when he was six, and the monks in the abbey near his village in Normandy had taken him in to work in the kitchens, as an act of charity. They soon discovered his ability as a scholar, even if they deplored his apparent lack of religious conviction. The abbot himself, who had first spotted the ease with which the boy galloped through his Latin texts, sadly reflected that Engeler's brain was, perhaps, too rational to take kindly to the mysteries of the Faith. The temporal world would also need its servants; so the monks trained his mind, and admired the clarity of his Latin hand.

By the time Engeler was twenty, the monks had nothing more to teach him. The youth was obviously outgrowing the cloister. The abbot commended him to the service of Bishop Odo of Bayeux. Engeler was enrolled in the episcopal chancery as a copying scribe. He liked the work, learning about the intricacies of ecclesiastical land tenure, and welcomed the greater freedom of living outside the abbey precincts. Odo deliberately tested him and found he could trust the young clerk's judgement. When the Bishop sailed with Duke William on his expedition against Harold of England, he left Engeler behind to help run his estates. No sensible man, not even a man of God, would leave his rents uncollected or his fields to be encroached on by unscrupulous neighbours. Engeler proved a faithful steward.

King William, as he had now become, relied heavily on the energy and the administrative genius of his favourite bishop in establishing the Norman ascendancy over England. Conquest was one thing – Odo was a fine example of the church militant – but imposing a permanent settlement on the English people was another. It needed firmness, of course. But, more than that, it needed other qualities to win over a stubborn race, proud of their Anglo-Saxon inheritance and customs. They were conservative people who set store by the precedents of their ancient laws. They resented foreign ways, feeling bitter that their old King (even if he was little better than a Danish adventurer) had been conquered and slain in battle by a French bastard.

Ruling this unruly, occupied territory would strain all the arts of Norman government: a strong will to enforce the King's peace, backed by a military presence. It would need a network of castles from which force could be rapidly deployed; an effective system of justice, capable of establishing a respect for the law. There would have to be flexibility in grafting Norman practice on to the old English ways; a willingness to make it worthwhile for the English nobility to transfer their allegiance. This meant, at least at first, that William had to respect the continuity of land tenure. The Englishmen who made their submission to the Norman king had their holdings confirmed. The rebellious were dispossessed. Their lands, and the manors of those who died in the conquest, were granted to William's followers. It all needed careful handling.

In the first months after his coronation, the King mapped out his strategy for imposing his will over England. In detailed discussion with his Council, it was Odo who argued that most of the Norman knights who had followed their Duke across the Channel were more useful as horsemen. They were good with the sword, not with the pen. What the King needed, to make the settlement work and to raise the money for the royal treasury, was trained administrative manpower. The Council accepted this advice, and William ordered his officers to see to it.

Odo thought of his clerks in Normandy. That is how it came about that Engeler was summoned over to England. He was twenty-six years old.

When he landed from the tubby old cog at Bosham, the reeve gave him an armed guide who rode behind him to

Winchester, where the Treasury was established. He was assigned to the land registry, working alongside a mixed team of English and French clerks. In their official business they used the *lingua franca* of Latin.

Engeler knew the English clerks sometimes made jokes about the Frenchmen in their Anglo Saxon. He quickly realised that he would never be able to hold his own and do his job properly unless he made himself fluent in the language. He had taken lodgings with the Precentor. In the evenings, the old Englishman gave him lessons. Engeler enjoyed the outlandish sound of the old English words. He particularly liked the legends of Beowulf and the story of the terrifying monster, Grendel, slaughtering nobles as they lay in a drunken sleep in their hall.

Quite soon, he was able to take on his English colleagues in their own tongue. One day, when Engeler came into the chancery, a bearded clerk called Eofrith said, 'Here comes the beardless wonder.' Engeler clapped him on the back and remarked, in passable English, 'And if you're a good boy, I'll show you how to shave.' He never had any trouble with them after that. The Englishmen came to respect Engeler's ability, and they liked the way he was interested in learning about his new country.

For his part, he understood the importance of establishing a partnership with the English administrators. Slightly to his surprise, he found that many of the features of their administrative machinery and legislative practice worked well. Their tribal memory was essential when it came to dealing with disputes about the ownership of land or the assessment of land tax. The King's senior officials approved Engeler's work, noting the way he was able to get on with the English. He seemed to have the knack of handling complex cases in a way which left the parties, if not fully satisfied, at least with a grudging acceptance that they had been dealt with impartially.

★　　★　　★

Nine years after his arrival in England, Engeler was promoted to be senior clerk in the Winchester land registry. It was a popular appointment. Engeler offered his colleagues a feast, with Emsworth oysters, to celebrate. Bishop Odo presented him with a loving cup from which bumpers were drunk, to the detriment of official work on the morning after. But that did not alter the fact that, by then, Engeler had made himself a valuable officer of the Crown. The Great Council was regularly seeking his advice in handling the enormous quantity of land tenure appeals being submitted for royal decision. As a reward for his work, William granted Engeler a small holding of land at Bosham.

Bosham Church as depicted on the Bayeux Tapestry

During the reign of the Confessor, the manor of Bosham had been held by Earl Godwine. It was his favourite estate. Although an Englishman, he had (with an eye on the main chance) declared himself for the Danish Cnut. Under Edward, he had become one of the greatest, and most turbulent, magnates in the land. His manors stretched across most of the Southern counties.

Godwine had died fifteen years before the Conquest and his heirs were scattered. Feudal society abhorred a vacuum. After Harold's death in battle, it was natural that William should take Godwine's lands into the royal demesne. He had put one of his own servants in the place of Godwine's old reeve to manage the manor and its port. But he was glad to have somebody of Engeler's loyalty on the spot, to keep an eye on things. What was more, Engeler's patron, old Bishop Odo, was becoming awkward of late. It was as well to throw him a morsel from time to time.

In the summer of 1080, while the Court was in Winchester, Engeler swore fealty to the King. He took direct from him two hides of good farm land and an old Saxon house on the edge of Bosham manor, by the entrance to Bosham channel. The land had been held by one of Harold's house carls who, like so many from that part of Sussex, had been slain defending his lord in that desperate last stand against the Norman knights at Hastings. Since then, the house had been left empty.

In August, Engeler rode over to see his new property. It was a fortified farm house, with thick walls of flint from the beach at Selsey, brought by sea across Bracklesham Bay and up the Harbour, then loaded on to carts on Cobnor hard. The windows were slits and the front door was heavy oak, studded with iron. Even the long barn next door looked ready for a siege. Engeler thought it a place that had been built with pirates in mind rather than comfort. But its position was wonderful: it lay near the tip of the promontory between the Thorney and the Bosham channels. From the upper room in the tower, Engeler could look down the Harbour and see the outline of the Isle of Wight on the horizon. The locals, he learnt, called his new home Cobnor.

Over the next few years, Engeler settled in to Cobnor and spent the summer months there, his junior clerks bringing work over to him from Winchester. The locals accepted him because he treated them well. Quite apart from that, it was always useful to know someone who had the King's ear. After a while, they began to bring their grievances to Engeler and ask him to intercede on their behalf.

Engeler reckoned the Bosham men were an independent, often bloody-minded, lot. They enjoyed mulling over grudges and muttering among themselves, mostly about land ownership, the payment of dues and ancient liberties connected with their use of the Harbour.

It was becoming increasingly clear to Engeler, as he read the appeals coming in to the registry, that neither the King nor his tenants knew for certain who owned what land and how much it was worth in terms of the geld, or land tax, on which the Crown depended for the management and defence of the realm. The old Saxon records in the chancery were hopelessly inadequate, and there was a strong suspicion that the Crown was not receiving the revenues that were due. The pressure for a more detailed and accurate picture of the holding of land in England, however, did not only stem from the needs of the tax collectors. The landowners themselves, whether they were English or French, needed to know the facts, have their titles confirmed and end the uncertainty surrounding so many of their estates. Particularly in the chaos following the invasion, there had been plenty of men on the make, English as well as Norman, who had grabbed as much land as they could get away with. There was, in fact, a common Anglo-Norman interest in knowing where they stood.

After talking it over with his fellow clerks, Engeler put up a memorandum to Bishop Odo, setting out the issues involved and recommending that a survey be carried out in every county, to record who owned what, and what it was worth. As Engeler admitted when Odo questioned him about his ideas, it would be a massive undertaking, only possible if backed by the King's authority. The survey's success would depend on the co-operation of the machinery of local government, the sheriffs, their officers and the Shire and Hundred Courts. They would have to carry out all the preliminary work. Engeler warned Odo that the process of conducting the enquiry would throw up a great volume of appeals and expose a host of ancient quarrels.

Odo listening carefully, saw the force of Engeler's arguments. As it happened, King William had himself been pondering this whole question. He had a tidy mind and, quite simply, was curious to know what sort of country he was ruling. Apart from his need to raise money, he could not make sensible military plans without knowing how much knight service he was owed. When Odo put to him the concept of a great survey, the King was already half convinced. He discussed the plan formally with his Council at Gloucester over Christmas in 1085. It was agreed to go ahead.

Orders went out in the name of the King to all the Shires to prepare for the survey and, in respect of Sussex, to summon the Hundred Courts in each of the Rapes to hear the pleas in advance of the arrival of the King's Commissioners. These were men of the highest rank, charged with judicial powers direct from the King. As word of the survey spread, men spoke of it with awe as the day of judgement, a sentence beyond appeal, an enquiry from which not one ox nor one cow nor one pig was to be hidden. Everything was to be recorded in what quickly came to be called the Domesday Book.

Engeler was closely involved in setting the terms of reference for the Commissioners. They would require answers to precise questions. What was each manor called? Who held it at the time of King Edward? Who holds it now? How many hides of land has it? How many ploughs? How many villeins, cottars, slaves and freemen? How much woodland, meadow and pasture? How many mills and fisheries? What used it to be worth and what is it worth now? And could more tax be taken from it? There was to be no messing about.

As soon as he could get away, Engeler hurried to Bosham to make sure that everything was in order to secure his own holding. He swore his deposition before the Hundred Court and displayed his royal grant. He was not challenged, and the Sheriff assured him that his tenancy was secure. But a number of disputes were brought before the Court, most of which involved the ecclesiastical holdings. Although Bosham was a royal manor, much of the land round about was held by old Bishop Osbern of the King. Two of the bishop's tenants, Hugh fitzRanulph and Ralph de Quesnay, were widely regarded in the area as foreign upstarts on the make.

One spring morning, as Engeler was supervising the planting of a row of cordon pears against the south-facing wall of his barn, an elderly man rode up to the house and saluted him.

'Good morning, my master.'

'Indeed, a fine one. But I'm not your master, only a clerk.'

'I know that, sir. That's why I'm come to bother you. Would you allow me to seek your counsel? I should very much value it.'

Engeler showed the old man into the house and sat him down with a jug of ale. His visitor was English, seemed well educated and was not to be hurried. They talked for a moment about the varieties of pear the Normans had brought over with them, and the merits of grafting their rootstocks on to quince. Then, looking straight at Engeler, the Englishman came to the point.

'My name is Aelfric, son of Icca, and my family has lived for generations near Cnut Mill* at the head of this creek. I was one of Cnut's thegns and, though I never cared much for Harold, I

* Now known as Cut Mill

45

would have fought with him at Hastings if I had not broken my leg out riding. I missed what must have been a good fight, even if our men could not withstand your armour. But I did help to bury Harold privately, alongside Cnut's little daughter, under the nave of Bosham church after the battle.

'For three generations we have held our land, not that there's much of it, from the Bishop. Since the dear Confessor's time that has been Osbern. But he's old now, like me, and too infirm to protect his own. One of your barons, Hugh fitzRanulph, has laid claim to half my holding and produced false witnesses in court to vouch for his impudence. I have heard of your knowledge of these matters, and my friends tell me you are a just man. I have come to ask for your help in preventing me from being robbed.' Engeler had heard many such speeches. He had learnt by experience not to take sides in land cases without first making careful enquiries. But he liked the straightforward way the old man had spoken. He also knew Hugh by reputation as a grasping trouble-maker.

'You do me honour by coming to my house, even if you flatter me by supposing I can help. But, having heard your story, allow me to take some soundings and see what I can do. Give me three weeks and I will let you know how I get on.'

Aelfric considered this a very fair reply. He finished his ale and Engeler watched him ride away.

Engeler thought about what Aelfric had said. He knew the success of Domesday would depend on the co-operation of the English landowners. If men like Aelfric saw that they could expect justice from the survey, it could make a big difference. The news of one wrong righted would spread far and wide. So he decided to help, establishing that Hugh had never been granted land at Cnut Mill. The reeve produced the old geld records to show that Aelfric's family had paid the land tax in full since Edward's time. Engeler then rode over to Chichester and to call on the old Bishop.

Osbern had found the young Norman clerk helpful to him in the past. He gave him his blessing and admitted at once that he had never held land at Cnut Mill from the King; and he gave Engeler a deposition, with his seal upon it, declaring that Hugh had no title to it. Engeler took this to the Hundred Court; and the jury agreed that Aelfric's title must be upheld. That decision would be recorded and the Commissioners would be advised accordingly. The next day the Sheriff served notice on Hugh that he must accept the Court's ruling.

Engeler rode up to the mill house at the top of Bosham creek to give the news to the old man. A servant showed him into the hall where a girl was sitting at her sewing. The light from the open door shone on her long, fair hair and, as she got up to welcome him, Engeler thought he had never seen so sweet a smile. He had never had much to do with women. They unsettled him – this one especially. He waited for her to speak first. She waited for him, and the embarrassed silence lengthened. Then both spoke at once.

'Forgive me for …'

'I'm sorry my father isn't …'

And they both laughed. Engeler introduced himself.

'I know who you are because I've ridden past your house and seen you planting trees in your garden.'

'I wish you'd stopped and given me your advice.'

She smiled. 'What does an important Norman officer want with the advice of a simple Saxon girl?'

By this time, both were grinning at each other. And they might have gone on standing there, grinning quite happily, if Aelfric had not come in. He shook Engeler's hand and made him welcome.

'I see you've met my daughter, Alice, and I hope you may have some good news for this house.' Alice started to leave the men to talk their business. But her father gently bade her stay.

'My only child is my heir. Her mother died five years ago; and Alice is directly involved.'

They sat round the hearth and Engeler reported what he had achieved on behalf of the Cnut Mill family.

When he had finished, the old man sat in silence. And then he looked at Engeler.

'I have these twenty years regretted the coming of the Normans, even if I admit that William is a strong king. But you, Engeler, have done my family a great service, and one I shan't forget. Many of my friends will take heart from what you have done, and I will see they know about it. From now on, you will always be welcome in my house.'

Aelfric made Engeler stay for a meal and Alice fussed over him, making sure his cup was full. As he rode back to Cobnor in the afternoon sun, he thought it was very pleasant to be fussed over by a fair-haired girl with a bewitching smile. What's more, before he left, she had promised to come and give him some gardening advice.

★   ★   ★

News of the way Engeler had helped Aelfric secure the title to his land spread quickly throughout the Sussex Rape. In the weeks before the Commissioners arrived, he was kept busy with worried callers seeking his advice over the presentation of their claims. Along with the principal men of the district, the reeves of the estates, the parish priests and the local officials, he was called before the Hundred Court to help sift the evidence on which the survey of the area would be based. Old men rehearsed ancient boundary grievances; rapacious men sought to use the occasion to expand. But it was not easy to hoodwink the collective sense of what was right. The tribal memory of who owned what was long and generally accurate. Neighbours eyed each other jealously. The harbourside villagers knew each other too well to allow well-known rogues to play tricks.

Engeler found that the most contentious cases tended to be those, often from multiple estates, where a lay tenant-in-chief had granted land to a smallholder when the land was already held by someone else. The more complex cases could not always be settled in the local courts, and had to be held over for hearing by the Commissioners, from whose decision there was no appeal.

Haggling over the detailed returns and hearing the pleas took up most of the summer. Engeler was much in demand as an intermediary. Although he made a few enemies in trying to settle disputes, most men found him fair in his dealings. When the returns had been collected, the sworn oaths had to be heard in the Shire Court and submitted to the Commissioners. Once they were satisfied, they ordered a fair copy of the returns to be made and sent to the central registry in Winchester, under guard.

Engeler spent the next six months collating the entries in the land registry, clearing up anomalies uncovered by the Commissioners and preparing cases where they had sought a second opinion from the Council. Once all the returns were in, a team of scribes set to work making a fair copy of the entries in the Great Domesday Book itself. The pages of vellum were bound together with thread and, finally, laid before the King. The whole process had taken twenty-one months: a remarkable administrative achievement. Engeler was glad that William was able to see his work completed just before he died.

There were no unpleasant surprises in the Domesday entries for Bosham. King and Bishop had their manors confirmed, as was Engeler's holding. Nor were the two Norman knights allowed to encroach on their neighbours. Aelfric and his daughter rode over to Cobnor with a brace of fine sea trout, netted from the Mill pool, and Engeler showed them the trees he had planted as a windbreak to shield the house from the south-west. That autumn, he saw much more of Alice. Their favourite walk was along the shoreside path around Cobnor point. He loved to hear her talk about the Harbour and its legends. She had grown up with them and they were as real to her as the history itself.

One afternoon, on the footpath opposite the spot where she said the Vikings had jettisoned the bell, Engeler asked Alice to marry him. It was blowing a gale and she pretended she hadn't heard the question. He had to put his mouth very close to her ear to make sure she understood. When he took her home to seek her father's blessing, the girl's face was still glowing from the wind.

They were married in Holy Trinity church at Bosham on 12 December, 1087. Afterwards, Aelfric invited all the men of

Bosham and Cobnor, with their families, to a great wedding feast. Aelfric made a speech. He proposed that, as Engeler was now becoming an honest man by marrying a good Bosham girl, and since he had proved himself a good friend to many of them over the Domesday business, they should elect him formally a Man of Bosham. The whole company banged their mugs on the wooden tables in approval. Engeler could never remember what he said in reply. But from that day on, all his neighbours treated him not as a Norman but as one of their own.

THE MUD

The Harbour's most priceless asset is its mud. The mud is astonishingly bountiful. It provides the base for the chain of food and nutrients on which the Harbour's living things depend; and its glutinous softness protects the natural quality of the estuary which development, in its various forms, could so easily destroy. Wise management has helped to keep the Harbour a place of beauty. But without the mud it might, by now, have been spoilt.

Each cubic metre of the grey glue is alive with creatures, most of them minute and unseen, burrowing deep down in the dark. Some of the mud dwellers, like the crabs and the flounders, hide on its surface, blending into the background, waiting to pounce. Some hide their bodies or their shells in the mud but let their feelers and tentacles and fronds wave in the water, to act as miniature fishing nets or early warning systems. Some betray their presence, when the tide is out, by leaving blow holes or casts behind them. Many, like the worms, are moveable feasts, eating the mud as they tunnel through it.

All these mud larks, fauna and flora, survive by living off each other. To sustain their survival, they have created a natural linkage between the different parts of the system. If, through some natural disturbance or change in the habitat, the balance is altered, the components of the system can arrange themselves into a new pattern. They evolve. But if the chain is threatened or destroyed by man, by his greed or his ignorance, the whole ecology of the Harbour suffers. It may never recover.

The mud does more than shelter and feed its own. The Harbour's birds and fish, as well as its grasses and weed, its reeds and saltmarsh flowers all feed on it. Without the mud they would have to search for other feeding grounds, or else they would die. The plants sink their tendrils into its moisture and nutrients, often holding together the edges of the channels in the lattice work of their roots. Sometimes the different grasses compete for the mud's bounty. The Spartina dies back, exposing the mud banks, and the green blanket weed, unnaturally fertilised by agricultural nitrates, invades the heads of the creeks with its smothering layer. Each plant, its seeds scattered at random by the wind or the water, is the creature of chance: pure luck plays its part in the rhythm of life and death, as well as the survival of the fittest.

The bottom-feeding fishes find their food on the mud pastures: crabs and worms, shellfish and shrimps. The predators are the cod and pouting, the grey mullet and bass, the schools of bream, coming into the Harbour in the summer, and the whole tribe of flatfish. The fish scavenge their way up the creeks on the rising tide, grazing over the mud flats as they go.

The sea birds feed on the mud with greater discrimination. They have their appointed pecking order. Nature has designed them to feed in different ways, often at different levels of mud, to ensure each gets his fair share. The tiny dunlin skip along the edge of the tide, picking at morsels. The oyster catchers delve deeper. The larger waders, like the curlew, with their long curved beaks, can dig deeper still. The wildfowl of the Harbour use the mud as their vegetable patch. The moorhen duck-dive between the reeds. The Brent geese honk down in their great skeins to graze on the saltmarsh grasses. And for the heron, solitary at water's edge, the mud is a killing ground.

On a damp night, when the moon is misty, the Harbour mud has a special smell. Not unpleasant, as some muds are. A tang of salt and sea-wrack, drying weed and the flowers along the shoreline. And all the time, as the tide rises and falls, numberless particles of that mud are washed to and fro, out to sea and back again, continually changing the depths of the channels and the whole shape of the Harbour. It is as though the mud has a life of its own.

Chapter IV

ELIZABETHAN

Ever since Master Drake had singed the Spaniard's beard in Cadiz
Harbour in the spring of 1587, they had been expecting it. But
the first hard news that the Dons were in the Sleeve was brought
by one of the Sheriff's men, posting through the night from
Southampton, galloping to Chichester to spread the alarm.

By the Queen's command, beacons were lit on the Downs
and the watch towers manned along the coast. Two years earlier,
when Walsingham's secret agents reported that a Great Design
against England was being mounted, two Commissioners had
been ordered by the Queen's Council to enquire into the
coastal defences and make recommendations for strengthening
them. They had ridden all along the coast between Poole and
Kent, taking local advice from the sailors and fishermen, siting
the watch towers themselves on the most exposed beaches and
headlands. The nearest was down at Hormouth, by the harbour
entrance. From there, a guard was well placed to cover the eastern
approaches to the Solent, right round to the Bill. Eastwards from
there, the next tower was at Pagham, although no sensible seaman
would try to land an invading army on those shifting sands.

It was all bustle as Sussex made ready for invasion. The Lord
Lieutenant had called out the Knights of the Shire and the levy.
The Sheriff had read out the proclamation of a state of emergency
at the Market Cross in Chichester. The Lord of the Manor of
Bosham was handing out staves and bill hooks to his tenants. At
the Anchor, the talk was of nothing else.

For the price of a refill, Bill Cambers was willing to tell the
tale. How he had sailed down the Spanish coast the year before

with Drake's squadron. Burning those barrel staves was a clever bit of work. Without those staves, the Dons couldn't fasten their barrels, and without the barrels they couldn't fill their holds with wine or water. They'd set back the sailing by at least a year. Bill had seen the great carracks moored side by side behind Cadiz breakwater, their masts thick as a great forest of close-planted pines. You never saw so many ships all packed together.

Bill had his audience by then, almost all of them seamen. Was the wind blowing Drake on shore? Did his ships anchor while the soldiers burnt the Spanish supplies on the quayside? Bill told them about the five treasure ships they had taken on the voyage home, off the coast of Portugal. He reckoned there weren't much fight to them. They lined their upper decks with soldiers in breastplates and pointed helmets all shiny in the sun, who sank like plummets when they pitched overboard. They flew great ensigns from their cross trees and they banged their drums and blew their trumpets.

A fat lot of good it did them. A bunch of popinjays, if you asked him.

'Our ships were smaller, without all that top hamper and gold leaf. We could sail twice as close to the wind. We had Master Hawkins of Plymouth and the design of his slavers to thank for that. But what really counted was our long cannon, down in the hull, with a range none of the Dons could touch. "Let the lubbers come", is what he said; "and we'll stuff their trumpets up their papish backsides." '

Bill's friends stood him another pot of ale.

Three days later, they heard the sound of firing off the Wight. Sharper than thunder, coming and going with the fluky so'wester that blew up the Harbour from the sea. People in the harbourside villages gathered outside their cottages and on the quays to listen and swap news. The Earl of Arundel had taken charge of the Sussex levies. At Dell Quay, the Chichester corn merchants had built a seventy-ton ship, the *John*, manned with seamen from the Harbour, to join Lord Howard's squadron off Spithead.

That night, some fisherman who had been lifting their lobster pots in the Looe channel had seen the flashes of gunfire over the horizon. There was no doubt about it: the Armada had arrived.

A month earlier, the Bo'sun of the Chichester ship had been going round the Harbour, signing on a crew. He sat on a bench on Bosham quay and eight of the Bosham fishermen put their marks in the muster book. Young John Cambers had wanted to sign on with the men of Bosham, but the Bo'sun looked at him and laughed and told him to grow another couple of feet. Then he'd be glad to have him.

'You've time, boy. There'll be plenty more chances, never fear. If it's not the Dons, it'll be the Frogs or the Hollanders. England'll need all the seamen she can find.'

John bit his lip. He was nearly twelve and had been out fishing and oyster dredging with his father, Sam, for the past four seasons. He reckoned he could handle their fifteen-foot Bosham punt nearly as well as his Dad, even if he admitted he wasn't quite as strong yet, when it came to hauling the net or pulling the heavy sweeps against wind and tide. But he could take her to windward down harbour as well as any of them.

John was very proud of their boat. He went down to the hard every morning before school to bail her out. When his father got home after the day's fishing, it was John's job to sluice out the bilges and stow the loose-footed lugsail in the Raptackle shed on the quay where the fishermen stored their gear. Even his uncle, Bill Cambers, who had sailed with Drake, said John had the makings of a seaman. Coming from Bill, that was a verdict worth having. John felt badly when the eight crewmen went off to fight, leaving him behind with the children.

Two nights after they had heard the gunfire, it started to blow hard from the north-west. One of those sharp summer gales, damaging because unexpected. The English ships had harried the Spaniards up the Channel in a series of inconclusive actions. Messengers had reported sighting the two fleets on the horizon off Beachy Head. Then came the news that the English Admiral had sent in his fireships, running before the wind in amongst the Armada as it lay at anchor off Gravelines, near Calais on the French coast. The Spanish carracks had cut their cables in panic to flee the flames; the storm had scattered them to the winds.

That was when an old man, out cockling on Wittering beach, had brought the news that a great ship had struck the Winner. Several of the Bosham men, including John and his father, had sailed down to the mouth on the ebb to see what was happening. For centuries unwary, or unseaworthy, vessels had foundered on the great sand shoal that spread seawards to the east of the Harbour's entrance. It was well known that winnings from a wreck had often made the fortune of a local family. There were even those in the neighbourhood who had the reputation of being professional wreckers, staking out their claim to a cargo with clubs and knives. Had the Winner, wondered John, got its name because of the winnings it spread across its sand?

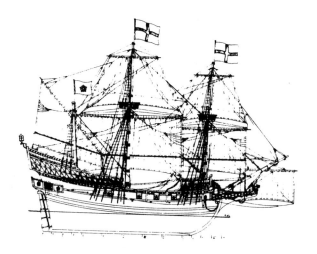

John's father brought the punt head to wind. She lost way through the water, her bows nudging into the shingly sand of East Head. John carried the anchor line up the beach and dug the hook deep into the dry sand. He always liked the feel of the soft white grains between his toes.

They walked round the Head along the water's edge. A flock of dunlin skimmed past in a shimmer of light, their wings brushing the sea. It was nearly low tide and furrows of sand stretched out ahead of them – mostly hard sand where they left no footprints; sand scattered with strands of brown seaweed, pointing seaward from their pebble anchorages; sand pocked with the casts of lugworms and empty whelk shells. Near the water, where the sand was still damp, there were soft patches, almost quicksand, where their heels left holes which filled with water. Along the high-water mark, the tide had left a more varied offering: cuttle shells, gleaming white, cobbles, sometimes pierced by magic holes, mermaids' purses and spongy clusters of decaying fish spawn. Every tide renewed its wrack, leaving behind purple jellyfish to rot in the drying breeze, and driftwood, smoothed and whitened.

When they rounded the corner at the hinge of East Head, they saw the wreck. She was lying on her side, about two hundred yards offshore. It was still blowing hard enough to whip yellow streaks of foam across the sand. The rollers were breaking over her hull and her masts had snapped off, leaving a tangle of rigging in the water. The sea poured in and out of her splintered planking, washing bits of flotsam out of the hull along the edge of the tide. A small crowd of locals had already gathered. Some of them had driven their carts into the water, close to the pickings: barrels, wooden chests, strands of rope, timber (many a Sussex barn boasted beams from well-seasoned ships' ribs). A group of Hayling Islanders had broached a firkin of wine and were passing it round as they sat in a happy circle on the beach.

John saw it first. A sodden bundle of rags on the edge of the tide. As they came nearer, they saw it was a body. John's father dragged it out of the water onto the sand, and rolled it over. John stared into a grey face with a matted black beard. It looked, the boy thought, rather like a cod's head, fringed with strands of seaweed. The man groaned. They sat him upright and he opened his eyes.

John begged a beaker of wine from the Hayling Islanders and the half-drowned seaman swallowed a mouthful. He muttered something that sounded like 'Grazzy', which they couldn't understand. The man was shivering now and Sam Cambers put own his jacket around his shoulders. The tide had turned. They couldn't reach the wreck, and all the worthwhile flotsam had been collected. Sam and John helped the stranger back to their boat. With a following gale and the flood tide under them, they were soon back in Bosham.

They landed on the little gravel hard by the Anchor and sat the stranger on a stool by the fire in the tap room of the inn. He steamed in the warmth and some colour came into his face. Sam told the company how they had found the man. He was obviously a foreigner, probably a Spaniard. Should they turn him in to the Sheriff's men? John's Uncle Bill considered. He had sailed with Mediterranean seamen. The Genoese were often signed on as pilots by the English captains. They knew the southern seas and the African coasts better than any northerners.

Bill brought a mug of mulled ale over to the foreigner and spoke to him in halting Spanish. But the man shook his head and answered in another tongue.

'He's Italian,' said Bill. 'I know a few words of it.'

Bill and the Italian began to talk, using their hands as much as their mouths – Bill, because he needed all the help he could get to make himself understood, and the other, because he was a southerner.

The rest of them in the tap room listened as the man, whose name was Mario, told his story. Bill translated.

Mario came from the City State of Ragusa* on the Dalmatian coast of the Adriatic. He was thirty-seven and had been a ship's cook, like his father, all his adult life. Ragusans rivalled Venetians as the merchants of the Eastern Mediterranean and the Levant. Their ships carried cargoes for anyone, even the Turks, provided they paid the right price. Philip of Spain had chartered fourteen Ragusan merchantmen to swell his Armada and Mario's carrack was one of them. The owner had told his skipper before they sailed that the crew would only be paid if the ship came back to her home port safely. (As Mario remarked, if they drowned, they wouldn't be paid anyway!) Their job, the Spanish Admiral had told them, was not to fight but simply to transport the stores for the troops the fleet was carrying to England.

They had hung around in Cadiz for months while the men and material for the expedition were collected. And when they eventually did sail, you never saw such chaos. The soldiers were seasick; the horses died; the water barrels leaked. Although their

* now Dubrovnik

ship had managed to steer clear of the English fleet which dogged them up the Channel, they had been dismasted off Dover and the gale had driven them downwind. Some of the crew had launched the ship's pinnace, but she was overloaded and had foundered. Only a handful of men were still on board the ship when she had struck the sandbank and Mario feared they had all drowned. After he had finished his tale, Mario stood up and thanked Sam Cambers for saving his life. He took a thin gold chain from his neck and presented it to John. The Bosham men liked that gesture and decided they would not hand the Ragusan over to the Sheriff. The landlord could do with a cook …

Even after the fireship attack at Gravelines, the Armada was still formidable. England had thrilled to The Queen's speech to her troops at Tilbury, when she had declared herself ready to take up arms with them, and to die if need be.

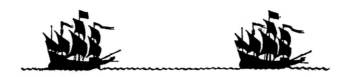

'I know I have the body of a weak and feeble woman,' – the soldiers reckoned if you believed that, you'd believe anything – 'but I have the heart and stomach of a King, and a King of England, too.'

They roared approval. But as Bill Cambers remarked, fine words buttered no Spanish parsnips. For days England's fate hung in the balance. It was the autumn gales that dashed Philip's hopes, as they dashed his ships against the rocks of Scotland and Ireland.

Amid all the rumour that swept the country, and the high drama at sea over the horizon, the life and work of the Harbour had to go on. The fishing communities would starve if the boats didn't haul their nets or lay their crab pots and bait their long lines. The weather was atrocious. For days on end, the rain pelted down and the wind swept up the Harbour, driving the salt spume across the fields on the lee shores. A grey seascape, the water flecked with foam.

It was on one of those sullen autumn days that the blood feud began. A feud between two good harbour families, one from Bosham and one from Itchenor; a feud that was to last, with bitterness, for generations.

Sam Cambers had taken John with him down the Harbour and they had done well with the mackerel near the mouth at the top of the tide. He judged that the fish would soon be moving into deeper water as the days turned colder, and today might prove the last time this season that they got in among a decent shoal. The floorboards of their boat were ankle deep in the catch. As the tide began to ebb, Sam hoisted the lugsail and ran for home.

Several other Bosham and Itchenor boats kept them company, running up the Harbour. As so often happened, the wind had freshened when the tide turned and the opposing forces of wind and water built up a nasty sea. Sam gave John the tiller, telling him to take Stoke Clump on the ridge of the Downs as his leading mark, while he began to gut the mackerel. The fish went off quickly if they weren't cleaned as soon as they were caught. John always liked taking the helm, feeling the bows slice into the water and watching the wake smoothing out astern. But dead before the wind in these conditions was tricky: lose concentration for a moment and the wind could get you by the lee. Then you could be in trouble.

Off Chalkdock point, the channel curved round to starboard and they would have to gybe. They were scudding along against the tide, about seven of the fishing boats bunched together. One of the Hone boys from Itchenor was single-handed in his oyster punt about two boats lengths off on the starboard beam. He waved at John. As John raised his hand in reply, he slipped on some fish on the floorboards. He let go the tiller. They broached and smashed into the Hone boat amidships. George Hone lost his balance and tumbled into the water. It all happened very fast.

Sam leapt forward and eased his bows off the side of the waterlogged Hone boat. He looked round and saw George's head bobbing in the waves. He was being carried away by the ebb. Sam made John sit amidships and brought the boat round close hauled on the wind. He had to reach the Hone lad quickly.

Not many of the harbour fishermen had ever bothered to learn to swim. For them, the sea was for fishing, not for swimming. He ought to be able to pick him up on the next tack. Sam put the helm down and the boat came into the eye of the wind. But she wouldn't go about. Her head paid off in the waves. Sam tried to tack again, pushing the tiller hard to leeward.

But she wouldn't answer. He got out the oars and pulled her head round on to port tack. By then, the current had taken George Hone much further down harbour, and it was some minutes after the collision before they came alongside him. Sam reached over the lee side and grabbed his shirt collar. John helped haul the dead weight over the gunwhale and on to the centre thwart. George lay with his eyes closed and a purple lump on his temple. He must have hit his head on his boat's coaming when he was pitchforked into the water. He was certainly unconscious. No … when Sam put a finger to his neck, he felt no pulse.

They sailed up to Itchenor in silence and beached the boat on the hard. Sam told his son to look after the boat and slung George's body over his shoulder. The lifeless arms flopped behind Sam's back as he staggered up the gravel. When he reached the muddy street that came down to the waterside, Sam shifted the boy so that he held him in both arms. The Hone cottage was the second on the right. George's mother opened the door and stared at her son, not understanding. Sam laid the body out on the kitchen table as George's father came through the back door.

Sam tried to explain what had happened. The father listened, without moving. The mother bent over her son. There was a long silence when Sam finished. The gale moaned in the chimney piece. George Hone, the elder, was a Puritan, stern and unforgiving. He held by the rule of an eye for an eye. The Cambers men, father and son, had killed his boy. He could neither show mercy, nor would he weep. The Lord, in his own time, would have His revenge.

He opened the door and Sam left. There was nothing to be said. All the way up the channel to Bosham, Sam reproached himself: he had sailed that day without the two pennies he could have placed in the poor lad's staring eyes.

Interlude

INTO HARBOUR

The spritsail barge had come round from the London river with a cargo of coal. She was deep laden and it had been a wet trip, blowing fresh from the south-west. The skipper had thought about anchoring in the Park, under the lee of Selsey Bill, and waiting till the wind and sea went down. But that would mean missing his tide, and it might go on blowing for days. The owners wouldn't like that. Time was money for them. He had a good offing and it would be a pity to bear away and lose all that advantage. The old barge went pretty well to windward with her leeboards; although he had to admit privately that, with her flat bottom, she wasn't brilliant on a beat.

So *Sophie of Maldon* carried on, into the stiff breeze, with the spring tide under her, pushing the old hull along. When *Sophie* had the Mixon abeam, the conditions worsened as they so often did at that awkward corner. Wind against the last of the flood, the sea came solid over her bluff bows, the heavy barge thumping down in the troughs of the waves. The skipper and his eighteen-year-old son were both soaked under their black oilskins. Still, they were used to that, and the Channel wasn't cold in September.

Once they got through the overfalls of the Street and had the Medmery Bank abeam, the skipper was able to ease sheets and *Sophie* lifted her skirts. It made such a difference, just a few points off the wind. Bracklesham Bay flew past. Almost high water now. The skipper kept well up to windward, to clear the East Pole Sands. When the harbour entrance was due north, he bore away over the Bar. He had timed it nicely. There was some swell. But not the breaking seas there would be in three hours time, when the full force of the ebb met the So'wester. If the wind didn't die on him, and he didn't think it would, they should be able to make it up to Dell Quay before they ran out of water.

Past Eastoke Point on the Hayling shore, and into calmer water, the ebb was just starting. They pulled off their stiff oilskins. The boy winched up the lee boards – they wouldn't be wanting them any more – and made ready the mooring lines. They gybed *Sophie* round the north-west edge of the Winner and left East Head to starboard.

The skipper wondered how many times he'd come into the Harbour over the past forty years. He ought to know the way by now. He was an Emsworth man. The sun came out and lit up the Downs as they headed up the Chichester Channel. He didn't really need to use Stoke Clump as his leading mark, but it was always reassuring to point the bowsprit towards it. Pilsey to port and then Cobnor, past the mouth of the Bosham Channel and the boy lowered the staysail and lashed it down. They were going quite fast enough without it. The topsail had never been set the whole trip.

One of the big Thames barges was transferring her cargo of coal into a pair of dumb barges on the hard at Itchenor. *Sophie* drew less and she could get right up the harbour. There was still plenty of water, though the ebb was stronger now. The wind was fluky through the trees up the Itchenor reach. They left Birdham to starboard and ran dead before the wind up Chichester Lake. Off Copperas Point, the spire of the Cathedral came into view, beckoning. The boy remembered his father telling him once that it was the only cathedral in England you could glimpse from the sea and how, in olden days, the builders had brought in the stone by barge. He thought about the times he'd dumped stone ballast overboard in the Harbour before loading a cargo of grain. Enough to build a row of houses. The skipper told him to wake up and jump to it and brail up the mainsail or else they'd hit the bloody spire and all. The boy led the fall of the halliard round the windlass and hoisted the clew of the loose-footed, tanned main up to the sprit yard. *Sophie* lost way.

It was suddenly much quieter up the Harbour. The ebb at the top of the creek was balancing the windage on *Sophie's* hull, and the skipper calculated, without really thinking about it, that he would just be able to make the Quay. He was glad to see no other vessels alongside. The quaymaster could be an awkward sod when it came to shifting berths. *Sophie* still had about four foot of water under her. She could lie against the quay tonight and the soft mud would never hurt the bottom. The old man leant on the heavy tiller and *Sophie's* bowsprit just swung clear of the end of the quay. The barge nudged alongside, scarcely moving through the water. The boy jumped ashore and took the stern line round a polished oak bollard, gently surging the warp until *Sophie* lay abreast the quay. It had all looked so easy.

The skipper lit his pipe and sat on a spare fender, while his son tidied up the lines on deck. He was a good boy. He'd take over one day. It was getting dark. The coal merchants' carts would be on the quay to unload in the morning. He and his lad might just nip into the pub before turning in. *Sophie of Maldon* could look after herself.

Chapter V

RESTORATION

The harbour people had never taken much interest in politics. The truth was that they were very cut-off from the outside world. It took most of the day even to get to Chichester on horseback or by cart. In the winter, when the floods were out, the journey was impossible. So it was hardly surprising that the harbourside communities tended to be wrapped up in their own, inward-looking affairs. The villages huddled round the separate arms of the Harbour seldom had much to do with each other. They kept themselves to themselves. Nor were they particularly good neighbours. Hampshire folk didn't mix with Sussex. The Men of Bosham had always been leery of Itchenor. And if you were a farmer, even if you lived close to the Harbour in a hamlet like Chidham, you faced inland and had little to do with what happened on the water.

So when King Charles was restored to his throne in 1660, it made little impact locally. Harbour people tended to like the old ways. It was comfortable to have a King again. They hadn't much cared for Oliver and his soldiers stabling their horses in the cathedral. Some of those old Levellers had just been troublemakers. And they were secretly rather proud that a harbour man had commanded the royal yacht *Fubs* when she brought the King's mistress over from France. Captain Darley had told some fine tales about that.

On the whole, the life of the Harbour went on much as it had always done. People gossiped about their families, about some vagabond in the stocks, who was courting and where all the fish had gone. They did like a good yarn. The loss of a vessel off the Mixon. Or that scandalous tale of that barrel of Emsworth oysters that had gone off and never should have been sold. The goings-on of the parson could make for a happy evening on a bench outside a cottage. Or the cack-handed seamanship of a son-in-law.

The subject that really got the Men of Bosham going, though, was the predatory behaviour of the Lord of the Manor. They'd got their rights, hadn't they? All set out in a charter with a royal seal on it. They should be free to use the Harbour as their families had for centuries. They wouldn't pay the dues for landing their catch on his bloody quay, and that was that.

Another thing that didn't change in the Harbour was the feud between the Hone family of Itchenor and the Cambers of Bosham. It was almost a hundred years old, and had become an established fact of harbour life. The two families didn't go around knifing each other or anything like that, They just cut each other dead — or cut each other's nets. Three generations had grown up since the incident that had started it all in the year of the Armada. Young John, the boy whose hand had slipped on the tiller so fatally, had died twenty years earlier; and his grandson, Nat Cambers, was now twenty-five.

Nat had grown up in the Harbour, half in, half out of the water, shrimping, digging bait and laying nets across the mouths of the little creeks that drain into the main channels. When he was fifteen, his parents had died of the Black Death. Nat had gone to live with his mother's sister, who was married to the miller at Cut Mill. They had been good to him, in a rather remote way.

Nat had spent much of his time alone, working his father's old punt. After three years at Cut Mill, he grew restless and when his father's friend, Captain Andrews, offered him a berth as a hand on his trading ketch, Nat jumped at it. He had often stared at the black-hulled *Elizabeth* as she leant up against Bosham quay. A powerful, full-bodied vessel, sixty feet on deck with a bowsprit nearly a third as long again. She worked the Solent, carrying whatever cargoes there was demand for. She had two bunks in the fo'c'stle and a pot-bellied stove in the cuddy aft, where the skipper slept.

Nat enjoyed his time in the *Elizabeth* and came to respect Andrews. When the lad had proved himself, Andrews made Nat his mate and gave him a small share in the profits. But that spring, Captain Andrews was so crippled with arthritis that he had to go ashore and the *Elizabeth* was sold to a general merchant over in Poole. Nat didn't want to work for a Poole man, although he was given the opportunity. So he was out of work. He hung around the Harbour, doing odd jobs, including a season dredging on one of the Emsworth oyster boats. He couldn't settle down.

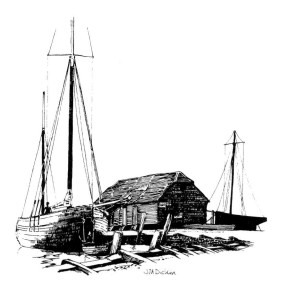

Now and then, on a moonlight night, he went out to snare a rabbit for his aunt's pot. Several of the local lads did the same. Late one evening, he rowed his dinghy down the Bosham channel to Cobnor, near the mouth, and walked across the fields to Chidmere. He knew the coppice there had a useful warren. He could see quite well with the full moon. All the more reason to take care. The squire had a rough keeper, who wasn't squeamish in the way he handled poachers. Nat crouched on the edge of the wood and listened. It was a still night. All was quiet. He crept into the trees, carefully brushing the branches away from his face. It was darker in here and he had to move slowly to avoid stumbling over a fallen tree trunk.

As he got closer to the warren, he thought he heard something. He stopped. It sounded like a low moan. Perhaps it was a wounded animal? He inched toward the sound. A moonbeam through the trees fell on a body, lying at an awkward angle on the ground just ahead of him. Nat knelt down and saw it was a young man. His left ankle was caught in a trap. Its jaws had bitten deep into the flesh and his boot was full of blood. Nat unsheathed his heavy knife and levered the jaws of the trap open. The man stifled a scream.

'Hold on while I get you out of here.' The man seemed too far gone to hear. Nat carried him out of the wood and over the fields to the dinghy and laid him in the stern. He bound a salty rag round the swollen, bloody ankle and dashed some sea water in the man's face. He opened his eyes and groaned.

'Let's get you home. Can you tell me where that is?'

'Over at Itchenor.'

'What's your name?'

'Hone,' the man whispered, 'Sam Hone.'

Nat stared at his passenger as he pushed off in the dinghy. A Hone! It must be the first time in a hundred years a Camber had spoken to one of that breed. But he had to get him home. The ankle looked in a bad way. Sam was clearly in great pain. Nat rowed down to Deep End, where the two channels met, and across to the Itchenor shore. He knew where the Hone family lived. He beached the boat on the hard and carried Sam up to his cottage. He banged on the door. The father came down in his night shirt, followed by an older woman and a girl. They helped Sam into a chair by the hearth. While mother and sister busied themselves boiling a kettle and collecting bandages, Nat explained how he had found Sam caught in the trap.

They made Nat sit at the kitchen table. When the kettle had boiled, Sam's father gave him a hot toddy and Nat had to tell his story all over again. The mother put a linament on the wound and bound it up.

Her daughter, Ann, watched Nat as he was speaking. Nat thought she must be about eighteen. She had dark, curly hair which fell over her nightdress. But what he noticed most were her eyes, looking at him so gravely.

'We are in your debt,' said the father when Nat had finished. 'And may I ask your name?'

Nat looked at him. 'I believe it is a name that will not please you.'

'How so?'

'Because I am a Camber, Nat Camber, of Bosham.'

It was quiet in the room for a long time. Nobody moved. Sam's father stood, looking at the floor. The mother put her apron to her mouth, Ann blushed. Of the four members of the Hone family in the room, only she kept her eyes on Nat. She was afraid of how her father would react. The mother scarcely knew what to think. The Camber boy had saved their son. But the two families had never spoken to each other. It had always been so. Nat sat at the table uncertain what to do. The father broke the silence.

'You must leave now. I shall remember what you have done this night; so will my son. But some things can never be changed. What is past between our families cannot be undone. I am sorry. But you must never come to this house again.'

Sam tried to rise from his chair, but he was too weak. 'Father, you can't just …'

'Stay still, son. Let it be.'

Nat's face was flushed. Perhaps it was the toddy. He said nothing. He picked up his jacket and walked out of the door. Sam's father hadn't moved. As Nat walked down the street towards the hard, he heard footsteps. Ann was running after him.

'I couldn't let you leave like that. I am so sorry. My father is a proud man. He couldn't bring himself to do what he should have done. Please forgive us.'

Nat looked down at the girl, standing so close to him. 'I understand. It was difficult. But thank you. I shall remember that.'

He went down the hard and dragged the dinghy into the water. As he rowed away, he saw her standing in her cloak in the moonlight, watching him go.

Nat told nobody about his encounter with the Hone family. But he kept on turning it over in his mind, especially the image of that dark-haired girl with the grave eyes, and the little wave she had given him from the hard. He was hurt by her father's behaviour. How could it be logical for him to be grateful for the way he had rescued the son, then, just because his name was Camber, to turn him out of the house? How long did it have to be before an ancient feud was forgotten?

All Nat knew was that he wanted to see Ann again. He realised a meeting would not be easy to arrange. Even without the feeling between the two families, there weren't many occasions when people from Bosham and Itchenor were thrown together. It was a surprisingly long journey between the two villages by land, and the local families simply didn't go visiting each other by boat.

A fortnight after the rescue, it happened that a large school of bass had been feeding on fry in the channel between Chalkdock Point and Deep End. Nat had gone out after them, driftlining with the tide. One warm afternoon, just as he had landed a spanking silver six-pounder, he saw Ann on the footpath under the holm oaks by the water's edge. It was nearly high water and he rowed up the narrow rife and jumped out on to the shingle. He tied his painter to an exposed tree root. Ann was standing about twenty yards away. Nat wiped his hands on his jersey and walked up to her. She was smiling.

'Good afternoon, Miss Ann.'

'Good afternoon, sir.'

They stood, together, Nat gazing at the girl. She was wearing a blue smock and carrying a posy of sea lavender. Her cheeks had caught the sun. She turned sideways to him, looking at the dinghy.

'You've had a fine catch.'

'Not bad. There were some good fish feeding off the point.'

'Shouldn't you be making the most of the tide?'

Nat smiled back at her. 'I'd done pretty well when I saw you on the shore. I thought I'd just come over and pay my respects.'

'That was kind, I'm sure. It gives me the chance to thank you again for saving Sam. I really am sorry that my father seemed so ungrateful.'

Nat looked at his hands. 'It can't be helped, though it seems a shame that our families have to go on with the old grudge. *I* don't feel it.'

'Nor I. What happened, happened long ago. It's best forgotten now. I know Sam feels the same.'

They chatted companionably for a while about nothing in particular, then Ann said she'd better be getting back. She was looking after her granny for the day while her parents had gone to market in Chichester. She'd only gone out for a breath of air.

Nat asked if they could perhaps meet again. Ann blushed and paused.

'I don't think my father would want us to. But this is usually my favourite afternoon walk.'

'Then let's hope the bass stay in the channel!'

He pushed the dinghy off while Ann walked back the path to Itchenor. He hoisted the little lugsail and hummed a happy tune all the way up the Bosham channel.

During the following weeks they 'happened to meet' several times in the same place. Once, again when her parents were away for the day, Ann brought with her some scones she had baked, and they sat on the tufty grass at the edge of the harbour, screened by the drooping branches of the oak trees. They were talking easily by now. About their families, their lives and their hopes.

Nat told her about his time as mate of the *Elizabeth* and how he hoped, one day, to have a little trading vessel of his own. Ann had been brought up in a family of boatbuilders and seamen, so she understood well what Nat was talking about. When he spoke a little about the loneliness he had felt after his parents had died, she put her hand in his and he kissed it. Not long afterwards, Nat declared his love, and they clung to each other, frightened to let go.

That night, as she lay in bed, Ann made up her mind that Nat was the man she would marry, whether her father gave his blessing or not.

Two days later, Ann's mother had a visitor. It was old Mother Dorling from across the way. She enjoyed the well-deserved reputation of the Village Gossip. She was given a slightly wary welcome. When she had sat herself down with some elderflower wine, she launched into the object of her visit.

'Dear Mistress Hone, how I dote upon your dear family! And how fast your little ones grow! I remember so well when they were born. And now, quite grown up! Why, your Ann is such a pretty girl. She'll make a fine wife before we know it.'

Ann's mother wondered what the old crone was leading up to. She hoped she wasn't about to suggest an arrangement between Ann and that dreadful Dorling cousin, the one who gave himself such airs ever since he had served on board the Royal Yacht. He had the morals of a coney! But Mrs Dorling wasn't leading up to that at all.

'I always have your interests at heart, my dear, as I'm sure you know. And that is why I thought it only my duty to tell you personally, so it didn't reach you indirectly, of something touching the welfare of your daughter. I do so with considerable hesitation. As you know, I'm the last person to be a teller of tales −' (Mrs Hone raised her eyebrows slightly) − 'but I felt sure you would not know, because if you had you would have acted already.'

'I should be glad if you would come to the point, Mistress.'

'Well, not to beat about the bush, I have observed Miss Ann together with that young Camber from Bosham. Two days back I was walking on the path down the harbour and I could not but help seeing them, quite plainly, sitting together on the bank. They seemed much engaged with each other.' Mrs Dorling paused and looked significantly at her hostess. 'Given the relationship between the families, I was confident that neither you nor Mr Hone would have sanctioned their meeting.'

Mrs Dorling then made her excuses and left, with the self satisfaction of a job well done.

Ann's mother wasn't sure how to handle the news. She might simply do nothing. But her husband would be bound to find out, from the old gossip herself if not from some other well-wisher. Better, perhaps, to tell him. She was less determined than he was to maintain his family's feud. She was a Sidlesham girl and had not grown up among the harbour quarrels. She had liked the way the Camber boy had spoken so modestly about Sam's rescue. After all, they owed him their son's life. Should that not be allowed to cancel out the original wrong? She went to bed that night debating the problem. Maybe the old woman had got it wrong. Perhaps it wasn't Ann at all that she'd seen? Or had Ann been with someone else? Mrs Hone was slightly frightened of her husband. In the end, that was probably what decided her to say nothing. But she determined to keep a close eye on her daughter.

Ann and Nat saw as much of each other as they could during the rest of the summer. When they were together, time flew by. The intervals apart seemed endless. Nat was increasingly concerned that Ann's parents would get to know that they were seeing each other and would order Ann to break off their relationship. One day, it all came to a head.

Inevitably, Ann's father was told. He was angry with his wife when she confessed she had heard the gossip but hadn't wanted to worry him. That evening Mr Hone asked Ann if it was true she had been seeing Nat Camber. She admitted it. There was one of those awful family scenes over which it is best to draw a veil. The father forbade further contact. The daughter defied the father, announcing she would rather leave home than give Nat up. The mother tried to calm things down. The father grew red in the face. Ann rushed out of the room in tears. The row solved nothing.

Next time they met, Ann tearfully told Nat what had happened. They agonised over what best to do. It seemed hopeless. Nat thought they would never manage to get Ann's father to change his mind. Maybe the only solution would be to run off together.

That night, while he was having a gloomy pint in the Anchor, Nat got talking with a neighbour who was full of the news of an expedition, fitting out at Portsmouth for the Americas. The word was out that they were looking for young men and women to settle the newly-planted colony of Massachusetts. Three ships were sailing within the month and there were still a few vacancies. The costs of the passage could be paid off over a period. Skilled carpenters and seamen were especially in demand. Nat's neighbour had recently lost his young wife and he told Nat that he was seriously thinking of applying. He wanted to make a fresh start and he reckoned the prospects were good.

'What about you?'

Nat said he'd think about it. The more he thought, the more he liked the idea. Ann and he could start a new life together. But what would she say? Nat could hardly wait to ask.

They were only able to meet for a moment, right down at East Head, among the dunes and out of eye sight. Breathlessly, Nat told Ann what his friend had said about America. She said nothing for a long time, keeping Nat's hand on her lips. She looked across the water to Pilsey. It would mean leaving her home and everything she knew. But she could see little future for them here.

'Let's go, Nat! Let's do it. I'm sure they'll have preachers in Massachusetts. We could get married there.'

Big decisions are often taken quite simply and quickly. They both felt excited, but at peace within themselves, once the decision was made. The next day, Nat got a lift to Portsmouth on a cart and found the quay where the ships were provisioning for the voyage across the Atlantic. The Captain of the expedition was short-handed. Willingly, he signed on Nat as an able seaman, having read the testimony old Captain Andrews had written for him when he had left the *Elizabeth*. Nat was able to get his agreement to take Ann as a passenger in exchange for his seaman's wages. The Captain told them to report on board the flagship, with only one sea chest apiece, in two weeks' time.

Nat gave Ann the news when they next met. He told her to pack her things at the last minute, on the day her parents went to market in Chichester. He would meet her that afternoon on the Itchenor hard in the dinghy. They would sail up to Dell Quay and catch the carrier's cart across to Portsmouth. The hardest part for her, Nat warned, would be to leave her parents without saying goodbye.

Ann hugged him. 'I'll send them a letter from Portsmouth to reach them when we've sailed.'

Nat told his aunt and uncle that night about Ann and what they planned, swearing them to silence. He sold his father's old oyster punt and counted up his savings from the *Elizabeth*. It should be just enough to start them off.

Neither of them knew how they managed to get through the next fortnight. Ann put her belongings together in her bottom drawer. Nat's uncle gave him his old sea chest for Ann, and Nat bought some warm clothes in Chichester. They said the Massachusetts winters could be bitter.

Ann's mother noticed that the girl seemed very much on edge. The day before they were due to leave, when they were alone in the house, she asked what was the matter. She suspected it was to do with Nat. She had increasingly come to believe her husband had been unjust to the lad.

'Are you keening for Nat?' she asked gently.

Ann ran to her mother and put her arms around her. She asked her to promise to keep a secret and her mother gave her word. Then Ann told her everything. Ann's mother held her daughter's hands and looked at her. She loved the boy, no doubt about it. She knew in her heart that her husband would never relent. Perhaps it would be better for the two of them to go off to the new world together than to be miserable apart at home.

She would miss the girl terribly. But her daughter's happiness was more important. She had given her promise. She would not tell her husband. And she would give Ann her blessing.

'Come upstairs, my love. You'll be needing some warm things to take.' Ann hugged her again.

The secret was kept.

The So'wester blew them up to Dell Quay in the dinghy. They took a last look at the Harbour from the end of the quay. The mud gleamed in the afternoon sun. And Nat, though he assured Ann he was by no means superstitious, threw a coin far out into the creek, for luck.

THE FISHERMAN

The old man hauled the heavy dinghy over the mud and into the water. Her rubbing strakes and keel left parallel lines on the smooth surface. Every year the dinghy seemed to get heavier. One day, he thought, he'd have to give it up. Not yet though. He wasn't too old yet.

He had timed it carefully: three-quarters ebb. Two hours before low water. Time enough to slip down to the point off Cobnor, get all the bait he needed to fish the tide, row down to Pilsey and drift up on the flood. He had the feeling that there were some bass about. All his life he'd fished the Harbour. He felt the presence of fish in his bones. If asked how that happened, the old man would shrug. He couldn't say. But the other fishermen respected his instinct, and his record spoke for itself.

He liked to think himself into the right mood for his fishing. He never hurried his preparations. His tackle had to be just so, with everything to hand in the boat; all the gear in its proper place. He bailed out the dinghy and stowed his clobber: a teak tackle box, a canvas ditty bag with a flask of strong sweet tea, a bar of chocolate, and his favourite greenheart rod. The rod had belonged to his grandfather Cambers. It had been varnished so many times that it glowed like an old piano.

He let the tide take him down the channel, now and then giving a touch on an oar to avoid the moored yachts. At Deep End he swung into the main channel and landed on the shingly mud bank that marked the outer spit of Cobnor Point. He carried his grapnel ten yards up from the tideline, burying it in the mud. Now for the digging.

Of all the baits a bass might take, the old man knew nothing more tempting than a large rag worm. There were those who argued the merits of squid, or even a smelly chunk of herring. Well, let them say what they liked. He would stick to a nice fresh rag, drifting free in the tide.

He took the flat wooden bait box and his potato fork out of the boat and squelched over the mud in his thigh boots. An ordinary garden fork was no good for digging bait. It cut through the worms. You had to have flat tines that held the forkload without breaking it.

There was a skill in choosing where to dig. Rags were not like lugs. They didn't give themselves away so easily. Lugworms left casts, little pyramids of squeezed-out toothpaste. Ragworms were harder. They liked a touch of shingle with their mud. You had to dig much deeper, two spits down, to find the big ones.

The old man started a trench just above the tide, carefully turning over each forkful. It was easy to miss the worms. The trench quickly filled up with water. It was always a good moment when the first rag was in the box: eight inches long and lively, its black nippers feeling for his fingers. Before he shifted to another digging, he filled up the old trench with the spoil. Some thoughtless bait-diggers didn't bother to do that and wrecked the best spots for the future. Some of the diggers were greedy, taking far more rags than they could possibly use themselves. But the worst were the ones who came down to the Harbour in gangs, digging the bait for sale. They had no thought for the future. Already, acres of the mud had been dug out.

After about three quarters of an hour, the old man had about thirty rags. That would do him. His back and his shoulders ached. He clumped back to the boat with his bait box, putting it in the stern; covering it with a damp bit of sacking to keep the rags cool. He coiled up the anchor warp and washed the mud off his fork and hands. The tide was beginning to flood. The dinghy was afloat. He sat on the thwart and rested. He decided to keep the chocolate for later. After a bit, he stood in the centre of the boat, pushing off with an oar. He put the oars between the thole pins and rowed steadily down harbour. By the time he got down to Pilsey, it was eleven o'clock. Conditions were good: a light Southerly, a soft day and most of the flood ahead of him.

He let the dinghy drift up the middle of the channel. Only a few other boats were about. He had a long running trace on his line, with a light weight. He baited the hook, leaving the ragworm's tail to hang free. He swung the bait gently in an arc, so that it dropped into the water about ten yards ahead of the boat, and reeled in the slack line, keeping in contact with the hook. The cork handle of the rod felt warm against the palm of his right hand. He held it lightly, keeping the rod tip up and nipping the line between thumb and forefinger. The trick was to try to think what the bait was doing in the water. It had to look natural, swimming in the current.

The sun broke through. It was warm and peaceful out there on the water. He rested his rod on the gunwale and took off his black oilskin jacket. He filled the chipped enamel mug and had a sip of the sweet tea. Just as he was putting the mug down on the thwart, the rod tip jerked. He picked up the rod, waited a few seconds and tightened. Nothing. Probably a little school bass. They were a nuisance. He reeled in. The bare hook shone in the sunlight. There was a strand of weed on the lead. The old man baited the hook again and cast out.

The fisherman concentrated on his line while the tea grew cold in his mug. The tide had carried the boat up to Deep End when his rod gave a thump. A good bite. He struck, feeling a heavy fish. He let it run out about ten yards of line before it turned and swam fast at right angles to the boat. The line made a zipping sound through the water. He put more pressure on the fish. It fought back stubbornly, boring down to the bottom, seeking refuge in the weeds. But the fisherman gave no more line. Gradually, he brought the fish towards the surface. Then for the first time he saw it: a marvellous bass.

★　★　★

81

The bass had followed the tide up the Harbour, feeding as he went. He had been tempted by the fat ragworm; confused when he felt the hook in his jaw and the line pulling against him. But he was a confident, powerful fish, fighting with all his strength and experience. He knew instinctively that he should try to get down into the weeds on the bottom. He nearly did. But the pressure against him was too strong. He used the force of the tide on his flank to counteract the pull of the line. Weakening, he was being drawn closer to the surface. He saw the boat at the same moment the fisherman saw him. The bass spread his great dorsal fin and made a last desperate lunge away from his enemy. It was no good. He felt himself being lifted out of the water in a net, gasping. Then, nothing.

★   ★   ★

After that last lunge, the old man knew that the bass had used up all his strength. He drew the fish over the net and lifted it into the boat. It was heavy. He laid it on the floorboards and knocked it on the head with his wooden priest. He took out the hook, wiping his hands on some cheese cloth. It was a beautiful bass, a good six pounds, the best he'd had that season. As he admired his catch, with its silver scales glinting in the sun, its brightness began to fade. The old man felt a curious sense of loss.

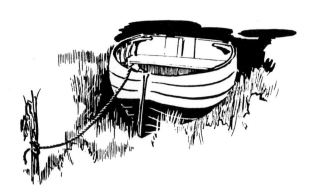

1 *The Creek, where John found the Roman coin under the bridge.*

2   *Looking up to Dell Quay, where Marcus built his cottage.*

3   *The Mud, sculpted by the tide.*

4 *Sunset over the Harbour.*

5 *Ragworm territory.*

6 *Tidelines.*

7 *Roots laid bare by the tide.*

8 *Bosham Quay, where the Vikings carried off the bell.*

9 *The final berth.*

10 *Early morning mist.*

11 *Down channel from Bosham, where Old Lob watched the Viking ship.*

12   *Down channel from the Quay.*

13   *Near the dunes at East Head, where the Spanish galleon was wrecked.*

14   *The Harbour, watercolour by Diana Thomas.*

Chapter VI

GEORGIAN

When his father died, Abe Appleton had inherited the boat he had crewed in since he was a boy. He had grown up in her. She was a sixteen-foot Bosham punt, clinker-built and heavy. She had been in the family for half a century. They used to say she could find her way around the Harbour blindfold. Abe was proud of the old boat. But even he had to admit, although he would dare anyone to say so to his face, that she was past her prime. Despite all the layers of pitch, too many of the planks below the waterline were rotten. When he took her to windward, the hull twisted like an eel and Abe had to bail like fury to keep pace with the water spurting through the seams.

He really needed a new boat. The trouble was money. He reckoned it would take at least another four seasons before he could go to his cousin's boatyard on Quay Meadow and place the order. A fisherman's takings were meagre, even in a good oyster season. By the time the carter and the fishmonger in Chichester had taken their cut, and after he had bought a new net, there was little enough left over.

That was what turned Abraham Appleton to smuggling. He simply had to have the money for the new boat. Fishing was the only trade he knew; without a boat, he would starve. He didn't even hesitate when they asked him to help. They knew he needed the money.

When it came to the point, not many of the harbour men hesitated. The men of Bosham and Dell Quay had never paid much heed to authority. They clung to ancient rights and freedoms granted to them in the Medieval charters. Customs duties and such like were for the rich to pay, not them. There had been free trading in the Harbour for as long as men could remember. Weren't they also doing a public service? Just because of the war with France, the gentry saw no reason to go without their brandy. It was a bit of a lark, too. A night's run made a change from the tedium of shooting nets and baiting long lines. But the great thing about a spot of smuggling was this: you could make more in a night than in a whole month of fishing.

Talking it over with his friends of an evening on the quay, Abe reckoned well over half the fishermen he knew had brought a cargo over the beaches on a dark night, or floated a four-gallon tub in through the mouth on the flood. Some of the men made a profession from the trade – as well as their fortunes. It was common knowledge that old Henry Cambers had done so well out of Hollander gin that he married a corn merchant's daughter from Storrington, bought himself one of those fancy new Pallant houses in Chichester and set himself up as a gentleman. Everyone knew where his money came from. Nothing proved, though.

The truth was that smuggling was part of Sussex life, not just the Harbour's. It needed capital to fit out and man a smart lugger, able to show a pair of heels to the Revenue cutters. It took ready money to encourage the riding officers to keep clear of a creek on a particular night when the tide served. Safe houses with secure cellars; a network of middlemen; reliable men who could keep their mouths shut and who could handle a train of pack horses quietly. It all required contacts, organisation and funds. In the harbourside pubs they used to drink the health of all the Sussex lawyers and parsons and their wives who were hard of hearing when the horses trotted by on a stormy night.

Abe was under no illusions: it was a risky business. The French war had certainly raised the profits. But over the past few years the government had imposed harsher penalties and strengthened the Excise Service. Revenue cutters, based in Cowes, were paying random visits to the Harbour. Last month, one had anchored in the lee of East Head and had nabbed Joe Andrews as he was floating a line of barrels up to Prinsted. There was even talk of a permanent coastguard on watch at the entrance.

Abe had to admit that some of the gangs had gone too far. There had been some very ugly incidents recently, giving the trade a bad name. The whole harbour community had been shocked at what had happened at Dell Quay three years earlier. A party of riding officers from Portsmouth had intercepted a cargo being unloaded across the saltings up at Dell Quay by a gang from Crowhurst (not local men). There had been a vicious struggle in the dark. One of the officers was stabbed to death. Seven others were clubbed on the head and wounded. The smugglers had trussed the excise men up, dragged them down to the edge of the channel and tied their wrists and ankles to stakes driven into the mud. The gang rode off, leaving the seven men to drown as the tide slowly crept over them.

The county was outraged. The Duke had insisted that something be done. Magistrates were handing down savage sentences at Assizes. The convict ships were crammed. Even reasonably honest men were swinging from the gibbets set up at crossroads as a warning.

Nevertheless, when the proposition was put to him, Abraham Appleton signed on. They wanted a strong man who knew the Harbour, with a small boat. His job would be to transfer the contraband from the lugger to the shore. The vessel would have sailed over from Holland or France with the goods hidden below a false keel or under a pile of oysters. As they reached soundings, the smugglers might have lowered a string of small barrels, towing them astern, ready to cut the tow rope if challenged. They told him that, after a few runs, he would have no trouble ordering his new punt.

Abe was twenty-four when he did those first runs. He had always been a bit of a wild lad. Bosham fishermen weren't surprised when he got the new punt, nor when he took to setting off from the quay on an evening tide and not getting back until dawn. Not much could be kept secret in that closed community. They knew.

That first season, Abe ferried five cargoes ashore. They worked different creeks: Thorney, Bosham Hoe, Longmore Point opposite Birdham, where there was a useful shingle hard. Other gangs worked the Hayling shore or, on a calm night, ran their vessel aground on the Wittering beach, the pack horses up to their bellies in the sea.

Abe liked the creeks at night. He had to make the tide work for him. He dropped down the Bosham channel on the last of the ebb and drifted up to the top of that night's creek with the new flood. He aimed to lower his grapnel as near as he could judge the lugger would moor. She would need a good three feet under her bottom at low water. Then he waited, with the night mist swirling around him, the tang of the mud and an owl hooting in the copse.

They had given him a repeater watch. Just before the hour set for the drop, Abe lit the spout lantern, pointing its narrow beam down channel, flashing on the withies that marked the deeper water. He heard the lugger's sweeps before he saw the outline of her rigging against the stars. Sound travelled a long way on a still night. She rode to her anchor close by Abe's punt, her hull deep in the water. He glided alongside, not a word spoken. The crew lowered over the side the puncheons and barricoes, the oilskin-wrapped bales of silk and lace, and the chests of tea and tobacco. Abe sculled the cargoes to the water's edge. He only saw the dark outlines of men who carried the loads to the horses. Then, they were away. Up over the Downs to the hiding places, along the sunken lanes, guided by shepherds holding their crooks in a special way of warning if the excise men were near. Abe never did know who he was working for. But, at the end of each run, when he came alongside the lugger for the last time, the silver coins were passed over the taffrail as the vessel won her anchor and gathered way.

There was not a moment to lose if the gentlemen were to be out of the Harbour before first light.

That winter, the lugger was short-handed. One of her crew had been caught making a drop in a spinney north of Petworth. It turned out that the man had been unfaithful to his wife, an unloveable harridan. She had betrayed him to an informer in the pay of the Excise men. A posse had been lying in wait for the smugglers as they arrived at the wood to bury their load.

The lugger's skipper asked Abe if he would fill the berth, just for a few runs across to France, until he signed-on a regular replacement. The pay would make it worth his while, provided he didn't blow it all on the cross-Channel attractions. He planned to run some cargoes from Le Havre into the Harbour during the new moon.

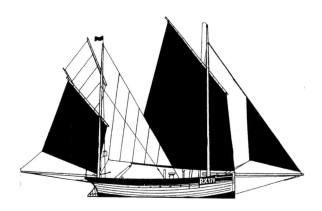

Abe had never been to France. They said the girls were partial to the traders. So he agreed and joined the lugger ten days later, as she lay at anchor off Copperas Point after a drop. There was an hour to wait before the ebb began. Abe left his punt drawn up on the shingle under the grassy little headland. He was sculled out to the *Mary Anne* in her jolly boat. The lugger was forty-five feet on deck, with a bowsprit a third of her length again. She was a Deal boat, and had spent most of her life servicing the merchantmen waiting in the Downs for a fair wind down Channel. She set an easily managed spread of canvas from her three masts: two dipping lugsails and a standing lug on the mizzen. Off the wind, with her sails goose-winged, the *Mary Anne* could fairly fly. Nothing could touch her. But to windward, she was vulnerable. A well-sailed Revenue cutter (and most of them were sailed like racing yachts) with her fore and aft rig could eat into the wind on a beat. The cutter's plank-on-edge hull cut through the short chop of the Channel, her lee rail awash. She could overhaul a lugger to windward in anything like a whole sail breeze.

The tide turned at the top of the channel and, with the first of the ebb under her, *Mary Anne* ghosted down harbour in the night, out over the bar, the outline of the Island barely visible. She set course, 150°+ Magnetic, for the Banc de Seine. A moderate Westerly gave them a broad reach: ideal conditions for a fast passage. It was eighty-five miles from the Bar to the approaches to Le Havre.

On a clear night, they made their landfall in twelve hours, scarcely having to touch the sheets. They tied up alongside in the inner harbour. The Port Captain came on board for his customary *pourboire:* the *Mary Anne* was a regular visitor; a valuable customer for the local merchants. Dock hands loaded her quickly, wheeling the barrels and chests up the gangplank. Just time for a meal and some wine in a tavern on the quay, with some calvados from the local apples as a digestive, then a couple of hours' sleep in the cuddy and the lugger was off.

The return crossing was much less pleasant. The wind had freshened and gone round to the north-west, bringing sleet slicing into their faces. A cold, horrible Force 6. A beat all the way, the bows smashing into the Channel swell, sending sheets of spray right aft.

Abe, on the jib sheets, was soaked before they had cleared the land. It took them eighteen hours, short tacking, before they came up to Bembridge. Visibility was down to less than a cable. Being uncertain of his position, the skipper had deliberately kept well to the west of the Owers.

When they were off Bembridge ledge, they glimpsed the cutter, running down, goose-winged, towards them from Ryde Sands. Her white mainsail stood out against the grey Solent. They recognised her at once: the *Roebuck*, pride of the Revenue Service, out of Cowes. The skipper bore away until, with sheets eased, *Mary Anne* lifted her bows and surfed down-wind, scorching eastwards towards the Middle Ground off Selsey Bill. *Roebuck* followed in her wake, about half a mile astern and not gaining. The lugger's crew relaxed – it had been a bad few minutes. They looked forward, with some confidence, to losing the cutter once night fell. If there was enough water at the entrance, they might be able to hide inside Pagham. *Roebuck* would have a job getting in there.

Off the Bill, the sea grew more confused as wind and tide fought over the rock outfalls. The Mixon was always foul ground. *Mary Anne* was rolling heavily, over canvassed. As the crew looked into the murk astern, the lugger's quarter waves reared up. Her stern squatted as though the following seas were trying to claim her. It was blowing half a gale by now and *Roebuck* disappeared behind a black squall.

Suddenly, at the mast head, the mainsail halliard parted with a crack. The gaff and sail flew down to leeward in a shambles of rigging, dragging through the water. As it snaked out, the mainsheet coiled around the mate's neck, jerking him overboard. *Mary Anne* luffed up into the wind, a dead thing, wallowing in the troughs. They lost sight of the mate, struggling in the waves. Frantically, they gathered in the waterlogged sail and lashed it down on deck. Climbing the mast to reeve a new halliard was impossible in those chaotic conditions. Abe backed the jib and the skipper let her bear away until *Mary Anne* was back on course. But she was only limping along, and *Roebuck's* bow chaser crashed out of the gloom, a lucky shot tearing a neat hole in the lugger's foresail.

The cutter was gaining fast now, flying the signal to 'Heave to'. It could only be a matter of minutes before she was up to the smuggler. *Mary Anne's* skipper knew the chase was over. No point in getting blown to bits; no time to jettison the contraband, either. He luffed head to wind. As the way came off the lugger, *Roebuck* ranged alongside, grappling irons fore and aft, fenders grinding as the two hulls surged together.

An armed boarding party came across and bundled the four remaining smugglers down into the cutter's hold. The two vessels got under way, *Roebuck* leading, with a small prize crew aboard *Mary Anne*, both vessels well reefed down, slowly butting into the Solent past Seaview and Ryde until they picked up moorings in

the Medina River. The smugglers were taken ashore in irons and locked up in Cowes gaol, while the crew of *Roebuck* were issued with a double ration of rum.

The next morning, Abe and the other three members of *Mary Anne's* crew were hauled before the Magistrates. The captain of *Roebuck* gave his clear-cut evidence: contraband seized on board; the attempt to evade capture; the previous record of the lugger's crew. The verdict was not unexpected. All four men were to be transported to remain in a penal settlement for the rest of their natural lives.

Two days dragged by in Cowes town gaol, a stone hovel with a drunken turnkey, who only fed prisoners with the money to buy their food. The rest got slops. Abe's companions were a well-known local vagrant, an incompetent highwayman who had failed to spot a blunderbuss hidden beneath the guard's cloak on the Newport coach, a young man who had fallen foul of a well-to-do farmer for dallying with his daughter, and a poacher caught with a brace of pheasants and a hare in his pockets over by Ventnor. A typical mixed bag, none of them really vicious. All of them unlucky; all, in the judgement of the Bench, were better off out of England.

On the third day, Abe and the other prisoners were taken in chains down to the town quay and put aboard a Revenue smack, one of the maids-of-all-work servicing the Solent harbours. Her helmsman had been aboard *Roebuck* when she had taken *Mary Anne*. He recognised Abe.

'Hard luck, matey. No brandy for you! By the time you get to Botany Bay, you'll be glad enough for good, clean water.'

Abe grinned at the old sailor. 'So where are we bound now, grandfather?'

'Not so much lip, laddy. And take my word for it. Don't play the Merry Andrew aboard your hulk, or the bosun will have the last laugh. They can't abide clever boys on the hulks.'

He spat into the Medina and the ebb carried the spit past the smack's bow. So it was to be the hulks, thought Abe, with a long wait until the convoy of convict ships had assembled for the voyage out to New South Wales.

The little smack made the crossing from Cowes over to England in no time, a broad reach all the way. Abe gripped the windward main shroud in his manacled hands, bracing his legs against the slope of the deck. He breathed in the Solent air and let the spray wash down his cheeks. It felt clean after the gaol. He looked up at the curve of the mainsail and astern, to where the end of the long boom dipped into the quarter wave, slitting the surface and making its own wake as the hull flew through the water.

No wonder they had been caught by the Revenue cutter: she was even faster than this old plank-on-edge tub. You couldn't beat a fore and aft main with its spread of canvas sticking out over the counter.

Abe hung on, feeling the rigging thrumming under his hands. The helmsman had a patch over one eye. He wore a blue bandana to keep his hair out of his face. He gave Abe a grin – he looked as though he had run a few cargoes in his time – as he lent his weight against the tiller to counter the force of the weather helm. Both seamen felt the living hull cutting through the chop of wind against tide, the lee rail buried in the foam racing astern.

It was a brief moment of comparative liberty, a sudden reminder that Abe had spent all his life in open boats, his own man, beholden only to the tides, the sea state and the moods of the fish. But it was the smell of the salt water that clinched it. He knew he could never survive, cooped up in a convict ship. Whatever it took, he would have to escape.

The smack swept past Portsmouth Point and a mass of shipping spread across the harbour. Wherries ferrying passengers over to the Gosport side. Great East Indiamen, gold leaf decorating their stern walks, unloading tea and spices. Frigates in the dockyard, fitting-out for the Mediterranean, the petty officers harrying landsmen rounded up by the press gangs. Naval store ships, heavy with timber and pitch from the Baltic. Grubby trading ketches. Humber keels with coal from Tyneside. Smart, oared gigs, all a-sparkle, rowing Captains out to their commands anchored off Spithead. Lighters, pinnaces and bumboats, hawking their wares. Ships from all the harbours of the world, some with outlandish rigs: Dutch hoys, lateen sails from Naples and Genoa, even a squat and smelly whaler from Nantucket. Specialised vessels: a bomb ketch, her mainmast set towards her stern. An experimental ship, her designer hoping to solicit a contract from an immovably conservative Admiralty. A clipper out of Liverpool, lean and delicate, her towering masts well-raked aft, at rest after shaving hours off the North Atlantic run. Grandest of all, the battleships – their yards crossed, their black and yellow topsides gleaming, swinging in line at their moorings.

The smack threaded her way through the fleet until, at the top of the harbour, Abe saw the hulks. Old, rotting three-deckers, their masts cut down, their bottoms foul with weed, black hulls stained with rust and refuse. These were the saddest of all the varied company in Portsmouth. Unloved, neglected. They were manned by the cast-offs of the Royal Navy: time expired storemen; crippled seamen, grateful for any job; brutal bullies who enjoyed the gaoler's power; misfits who no self-respecting ship's company would tolerate on board. Quite a few had run from the Navy and taken new names. The Port Captain wasn't too fussy. No able seaman chose to man the hulks. They were gaolers, nothing more, guarding prisoners of war, or men condemned at Assizes to transportation and held in limbo until the convict ships were available to take the prisoners halfway across the world.

The smack rounded-up into the wind on the hulk's quarter. The crew made fast alongside. Abe was pushed through an empty gun port. The darkness of the main deck was split by shafts of light through the open ports, criss-crossed with iron bars. More light filtered down through overhead iron gratings. It was some time before Abe's eyes adjusted to the gloom. But the stench hit him at once. Filthy bilge water, smelly bodies, rotting food. On the main deck, the great cannon had been replaced by triple tiers of narrow bunks with eighteen inches between each layer. The whole space was filled with a jumble of figures sleeping, coughing, groaning, quarrelling, playing cards and mending clothes. More men were crowding round the open ports, clutching the bars, trying to catch a breath of fresh air – or the illusion of freedom.

Abe felt the eyes staring at the newcomer as a one-armed guard shoved him with the butt of a pistol towards an empty upper berth.

'Welcome, mate, to our cosy little home,' said a Sussex voice from the bunk below. 'What did they nab you for, then?'

'Trying to bring a cargo in,' answered Abe. 'What about you?'

'Oh, I was set up, I was. Good and proper. A put-up job. They wanted me out of the way. Simple as that, really. I'd had words. More than words. With the squire's son. He said as I'd been taking his Dad's birds and conies. His Dad was a Magistrate. So 'It's Botany Bay for you, you rascal,' says Daddy.

'Damn your false eyes,' says I from the dock.

' 'Take him away,' says Dad from the Bench. So here we are, matey. Shipped as well as shopped, as you might say.'

The man paused for a moment, then added, almost as an afterthought, very quietly, 'And all because a squire's son tried to have his fun with my young sister. But I stopped him, by God, I did!'

Abe's eyes were adjusting to the gloom. He saw his bunk mate was a strongly-built young man, stretched out on his back with his hands cupped behind his head.

'How long've you been here?'

'Twenty days and twenty nights. The nights is the worst. Nothing but sighing and cursing and coughing. The nights and the grub. Rotten potatoes and mouldy bread. We had three days when they took us in chains over Lavant way, a whole gang of us building walls. It was grand to smell the air. But then it was back to the hulk and an hour on deck once a day.'

'When's the convoy likely to sail?'

'Who knows? The scuttlebutt says there's two shiploads of our fellow travellers anchored off Bembridge now, only waiting for us to go on board, with an escort and a wind to take us down Channel.'

Two days later, on the early-morning tide, the escort vessel, a 28-gun frigate, and the fair wind arrived together. Abe and thirty other condemned men were rowed in barges across to one of the convict ships. She was an old East Indiaman, too riddled with worm for the trade and sold off cheap to the Navy for transportation. Swivel guns mounted on the break of the quarterdeck pointed down into the ship's waist. Marines, with fixed bayonets, stood guard over the hatches.

At noon, the convicts were paraded on deck for roll call. The First Lieutenant and a Marine Captain sat with the Purser at a table. The Purser had an open ledger in front of him. The Marine seemed thoroughly bored. The naval officer, thought Abe, looked a real hard case, a salt horse, come up through the hawsehole. It wouldn't do to try any tricks with that number. He'd seen it all.

One by one the men shuffled up to the table to answer to their names. Before Abe's turn came, the Purser read out two names without any response. The Lieutenant didn't seem concerned. A couple of felons more or less at the start of the voyage hardly signified. The odds were that they would have been thrown overboard before rounding the Cape anyway, dead of the fever, or killed by a fellow convict in a quarrel over a scrap of bread. Quite a few would have gone mad before the end of the passage. Perhaps only three-quarters would be well enough to go ashore in Botany Bay, unaided.

When Abe's name was called, he stepped forward and stood in front of the table. The Lieutenant looked him hard in the eye.

'So you're a smuggler by trade, are you?'

'Aye, sir'.

'Grown up at sea, have you?'

'Aye, sir'.

The officer stared at Abe. The Royal Navy maintained a curiously ambivalent dislike of the smuggling gentry. They evaded the press gangs with false papers granting them exemption. They made their fortunes, so the received wisdom went, while in the King's ships, sailors risked their lives for hard tack and a pittance.

Yet, no seafaring man could quite bring himself to bracket a fellow seaman with some snivelling landlubber of a pickpocket. This equation balanced in the Lieutenant's mind with a more practical consideration. The press had only brought in four miserable drunks, not one of them a prime seaman. He was desperately short of hands. Most of his people had signed on to get away from trouble on land. There were probably as many villains among the hands as among the convicts. This one looked useful; anyway, he wasn't about to look even a tainted gift horse in the mouth.

'We're shorthanded this trip. Give your word you won't be foolish enough to try to escape, and you can sign on, rated able, for the voyage. No irons. Seaman's rations. No pay. Back in the clink once we sight Botany Bay. Agreed?'

'Aye aye, sir.'

'Sign him on, purser.' And Abe made his mark in the muster.

The rest of the prisoners looked extremely sour when Abe and three other men, all obviously seamen, were led off to the fo'c'sle to be welcomed, in an ironical manner, by their new shipmates.

'Make yerselves at home, gentlemen. Stow the cargo over 'ere. Where's the brandy, then? Any spare baccy, cully?'

Abe grinned and raised two fingers in response. He knew that a number of the hands aboard any ship in the Royal Navy would have done a bit of free trading in their time. Envy of fabulous profits apart, the lower deck to a man regarded smuggling, if not as an entirely legitimate profession, at least as an ancient maritime occupation carried out in manly defiance of the corrupt sods who governed the country, and who kept their own pay in arrears. As seamen, the hands knew that to get a cargo across the Channel in winter in an open lugger needed seamanship. So it was no surprise to anyone when the Bosun clapped Abe on the back telling him, quite kindly, to join the starboard watch as a foredeck hand.

'Best you jump to it, laddy, and keep yer nose clean, and you've naught to fear from me. But play silly buggers, and you're straight back in the slammer. That's the truth.' Abe Appleton didn't doubt it.

That night, the Captain's steward, who always seemed to have the word before anyone else, passed on the news that the barky would be sailing on the morning tide. The last of the provisions were stowed. Two squealing pigs for the wardroom were hoisted up the side and pandered to by the simple, but good-natured, pig man, who had spent twelve years of his life tending the livestock aboard the same ship. The bumboats were sent packing, their exhausted female passengers resigned to soliciting fresh custom on Portsmouth Point. The ship's boats were secured amidships, double-lashed.

Abe slung his hammock and listened to the creaking of the spars as the ship rolled gently with the night breeze. The tide caressed the hull. Shadows from the lantern overhead swung across the deck. All around, men snored and shifted in their sleep.

Abe lay awake, trying to calculate the odds. It would have to be tomorrow, or never. Unlike most of the harbour men he knew, Abe was a strong swimmer. But where could he swim to and be safe? Once out of sight of land, there would be no chance at all. He gave himself evens: he was by nature an optimist. Tomorrow would tell. He rolled over and slept.

They won their anchor at dawn; a cold grey dawn, with the makings of an Easterly fretting the Solent. The early sunlight flashed green on the wooded shore of the Island. While the fo'c'sle party catted the anchor, the topmen went aloft and the sails filled as the old ship bore away down the tide in the wake of the rest of the little convoy.

Abe watched Cowes slide past – Cowes, where that Revenue cutter was based. Then Newtown, with its low entrance between the dunes, difficult to make out yet deeper than it seemed. Abe had done some good drops in Clammerkin Lake, just inside to port. Yarmouth (too well guarded for his taste). Then, looming white out of the mist on the horizon, the Needles marking the westerly tip of the Wight.

Abe was lying out on the leeward end of the topsail yard when the ship heeled to a stronger gust of wind. Nothing special, but just enough to shift his point of balance outboard. What happened then he was never quite able to decide. Was it deliberate, or did he lose his footing on the ratlines? All he could remember was falling, arms outstretched, down, down through the air, missing the ship's side by inches, a face on deck staring in horror, down into the shockingly cold Solent water, opening his eyes in time to see the rudder bubbling past in the green watery light, close enough to touch.

He kicked upwards, gulped in some air and floated, head down, a dead body on the surface, as his ship ran fast down wind, further and further away. He sucked in air and looked, one eye above water. The ship's stern was almost two hundred yards off. There were white faces at the taffrail, the flash of a telescope scanning the wake.

Abe knew how hard it was to spot a man's head, or a barrel, at sea, unless the surface was mirror calm. The odds were better than evens. A calculating captain would reckon that a man who had fallen from aloft would either be concussed or drowned by now. He wouldn't want to luff up, beat to windward against the tide and lose his position in the convoy, all on the remote chance that he might find a survivor. After all, it was only a convict.

Treading water, Abe watched the distance grow between him and the ship. The faces at the stern became blurred. There was no sudden scurrying on deck to signal that she was altering course. Abe's spirit began to lift. The prospect of a convict settlement took second place to the more immediate question of how to stay afloat. There was something in the water a stone's throw off. He swam over to it: a heavy wooden spar. He locked his arms around the timber and hung on. His fingers started to get numb and, after a while, he realised he had lost all feeling in his feet. But it was peaceful, hanging there in the water, and he thought he might as well take a nap. He must have nodded off when he felt his shirt grabbed from behind. Arms hauled his body out of the water and he was dumped on a deck. An elderly man was bending over him, shaking his shoulder.

'Wake up, lad, you're safe now.'

The man helped him sit up and the water streamed off his clothes. Abe was very cold.

'Get this inside you.' A pewter mug was held against his mouth. Abe choked as he felt the warmth of raw rum spread through his body.

'That'll put you to rights.'

Abe looked around, feeling strangely remote and light-headed. Was he really aboard this little fishing smack with this old man and a boy? The skipper was looking at him curiously. 'So what happened to you, then? Jump ship, did you?'

'No, I was out on a yard and lost my footing. They never turned back to pick me up.'

The old fisherman decided not to press the question. The young man's story might or might not be true. It wasn't his business. The main thing was that they'd been able to save a life.

'Lucky we came along when we did,' was his only comment.

The smack was beating up the Solent, skipper at the helm, luffing the boat through the puffs. A few dollops of spray came over the weather gunwhale when her bows pitched into a sea.

'We're over to Portsmouth to sell our catch. We'll drop you off there. No extra charge!'

The fisherman threw a tarpaulin over to Abe who put it round his shoulders. The rum and the relief did their work. He lay back on his damp patch of deck, falling dead asleep.

Abe woke to find the smack tied up to the fish quay in Portsmouth Harbour. He shook hands with the skipper, who brushed aside his thanks, saying, 'You'd have done the same.'

The old man watched as Abe climbed the iron rungs let into the quay. He thought that there was probably more to the lad's story than met the eye. He was a seaman, no doubt of that. No sailor with one hand for the ship fell overboard in the Solent when it wasn't blowing. Had he run, or been pushed? If he was on the run, there might be a reward for informing. But that was a dirty game. The old fisherman turned back to the job of filling the wicker baskets with his fresh-caught herrings.

Abe walked slowly along the bustling dockside, his damp clothes sticking to him. So far, so good. He was free. What to do now? He had no shoes, no money. He didn't know anybody in Portsmouth who could help him. He couldn't go home to Bosham. Somebody would be bound to go chattering in the

Anchor, then the magistrates would be on to him in no time. One thing was for sure: he had to find a job. No point in searching inland. He wasn't a landlubber. What he knew about was the sea. If he couldn't earn some money, he'd starve. There seemed to him no real alternative.

So Abe did what seamen down on their luck, or wanting to escape from their past, had always done. Asking the way, he presented himself, barefooted and damp, at the muster office by the dockyard gate. He gave his name as Abe Brown (the Duty Officer had heard that one before, too!), his trade, fisherman. The Royal Navy was far too short of able seamen to be over-inquisitive about a volunteer's past. Abe wasn't the first smuggler to find a home in the Service. The officer showed Abe where to make his mark. He put a firm cross against his new name in the ledger, feeling a great surge of relief.

Now he was safe.

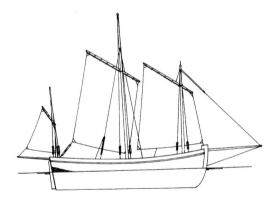

THE GRAVEL BARGE

Nobody knew how old the barge was. Maybe over a hundred years. Ever since the harbour people could remember, she had been around.

The barge was memorable, not because of her looks. To be honest, she was ugly. Slab-sided, box-shaped amidship, blunt at both ends. A push-me, pull-you sort of tub. Her timbers were covered in countless layers of thick black pitch, deeply encrusted with sand and mud. In summertime, the warm tar tended to melt, and all the barge's deck gear, her sweeps and warps and everything a man might handle was covered with a sticky, black paste.

The only way to distinguish her bow from her stern was to note that one bore a heavy rudder, trailing weed, steered by a long, curving ash tiller. Rumour had it that the tiller had been won in Queen Victoria's reign, from a gentleman's yacht. It was the one elegant thing about the vessel. A tiller to boast of, varnished over the years with so many loving coats that it shone in the sunshine like a burnished conker. The end of the tiller, where the helmsman held it, had been carved into the head of a greyhound, ears sleekly smoothed back, polished and softened by hands delighting in so beautiful a vanity.

What made the barge especially memorable was neither her looks, nor even her tiller, but what she did, and how she did it. She was a gravel barge.

A little old man owned her. For as long as people could remember, he had been old and little, his back bent from his labours. When you saw what he did, it was no wonder. The secret of the barge's life was that she worked the tides. She never had an engine. Only a

100

blackened, loose-footed scrap of a mainsail, two enormously long sweeps, and the tide.

The old man and his barge followed a routine; a rhythm set by the flow of the water in the Harbour and the direction of the wind. He cast off from the old quay at Emsworth on the first of the ebb, drifting with the tide down the channel to the Winner sandbank at the mouth. That might take a couple of hours. When he arrived, he either grounded the barge on the sand, or threw out a grapnel and waited until he touched. The barge's flat bottom kept her upright on the shingle.

Once the tide was out, the old man lashed a gangplank to the bows and wheeled a wheelbarrow down the plank. He chose a patch of gravel, filled his wheelbarrow to the brim, wheeled it up the plank and shot the gravel into the hold. He kept on doing this, steadily, never stopping, until either his hold was full or the new flood tide had covered the Winner.

Then, the old man would bring up his last load and stow the gangplank. There might be a good half-hour before the barge floated. He stretched his back and let the pain ease through his fingers. He went aft and opened a teak locker, taking out a dirty primus stove, which he pumped, primed and lit. He filled a black kettle with fresh water from a wooden beaker, and put three heaped spoonfuls of tea into a pint-sized blue enamel mug with four of brown sugar. When the water had boiled, he filled the mug, letting the tea stew. He never hurried the ritual. When the tea had mashed properly, the brew black and thick with tannin as he liked it, the old man squatted down on the little after-decking of his barge, to sip the scalding liquid.

By the time he had refilled his mug and emptied it, swilling the old tea leaves overboard, the barge had given the slightest of tremors, then shifted, like a hen coming off her nest. She floated free and swung round on her anchor to face the incoming tide and sea breeze. Hoisting the rag of a sail, he got in his anchor, then, partly sailing, partly drifting, let wind and tide carry the heavy load up-channel, right up to the quay.

Once the barge was moored alongside, the work started all over again. The old man had to unload the gravel. He used a small crane on the quay to lower a metal bucket into the hold. He filled the bucket with a shovel and swung it across to a waiting cart. Sometimes the carter's lad would give a hand, but mostly he had to do it by himself. He was used to it.

Chapter VII

THE TWENTIES

In those summertimes between the Great Wars, when many people wanted to forget, or not to think it might happen again, the Jazz Age elbowed its way down to the Harbour, disturbing the old rhythm of the seasons and the tides. New, often raucous, noises overpowered the natural sounds of the estuary. Time itself speeded up. Newcomers rushed about, helter-skelter. Speed was King.

Anzani outboard engines, belching blue smoke, raced home from East Head in time for cocktails on the lawn. Bungalows sprouted across the fields of Wittering and Hayling, boasting *Dun Roamin'*, nameplates in Olde Worlde lettering. It was charabanc time. At weekends, Austin Seven motors sped down from Surbiton, hooting their horns and coating the hedgerows with a film of greasy carbon. The wash from fast speed boats eroded the banks of the Harbour's channels, gramophones blaring ragtime from their decks. Overhead, biplanes with rotary engines did stunts and took trippers barnstorming.

In the winter, peace returned and the old pattern of the Harbour was restored. You could hear the Brent geese honking and the marram grass sighing in the wind. You could almost hear the shingle shifting under a spring tide on the ebb. When the Sou'wester blew the spume up on to the lee shore, the holm oaks along the edge of the tide squeaked as their trunks rubbed against each other and wore their bark away.

The winter dawns and dusks belonged to the wildfowlers, a special breed of solitary harbour men. They used a special type of craft, the duck punt, of which there were only a handful left in the Harbour. They were designed to do a particular job: to lie low in the water and to carry a large gun within range of a flock of wildfowl, without frightening them.

George Appleton of Bosham reckoned he had the best duck punt in the whole Solent. A regular miniature gunship, painted battleship grey, flat bottomed, with outriggers for the oars. She set a tiny brown lugsail to take her downwind — not efficient, admittedly, but better than trying to row back up the Bosham channel against the tide. Even the heavy gun was painted grey, partly to stop the steel barrel glinting in the sun; partly to protect the metal against the rusting salt air.

The gun had been in George's family for four generations. He was proud of it. His great grandfather had served as a gun captain in HMS *Albion* at the battle of Navarino in 1827, which won Greece her independence against the Turks. His gun crew had named their 36-pounder Bess. When the old gunner finally left the Navy, and had the punt built at his cousin's yard, he gave the punt's gun the same name, for luck.

After every outing, George unbolted Bess from her deck mounting and carried her home on his shoulder to the cottage on the Trippet. Bess was a wicked weapon. She scattered half a pound of shot into a bunch of geese at sixty-yards range. The gun and the punt were one. You aimed the gun by pointing the punt at the target. The difficult bit was to get close enough. The approach called for a skilled calculation of the effects of wind and tide on the hull and the birds. Ideally, you drifted silently downwind towards the birds as they were feeding on the edge of the creek.

George's grandfather had taught him how. You lay flat on the floorboards, sighting along the barrel and manoeuvring the punt with a pair of wooden bats strapped to your hands. The trigger had a cord toggle attached to it. As you closed the gap, the trick was to know how long to wait, how much closer you dared get before jerking the toggle. A good shot could kill a dozen birds. They sold well in Chichester market, especially just before Christmas.

George had learnt the hard way that he would seldom get a second shot on the same tide. There was only the one chance, so he came home empty-handed on over half his outings. There might be no birds; or wind and tide conspired to stop him coming into range. Or a Hayling wildfowler had got his shot in first. He knew it wasn't an easy way to earn a living, especially when a bitter January froze the saltings, his fingers stuck to Bess's icy breech block and his soaking clothes numbed his body. When he got home, he stripped and steamed in front of the kitchen stove. His mother washed the salt out of his canvas smock and hung it up to dry.

Despite its hardship, wildfowling was in his blood and he loved it. The trouble was it was a winter job and he hated the monotony of summer fishing: it was too slow for him. He was twenty-eight and wanted more action. So he pricked up his ears when one of the fishermen asked why he didn't try his hand at crewing in one of the big yachts racing at Cowes. It paid much better than the fishing. Your berth and grub were all found for you, and they gave you a smart navy blue jersey with your yacht's name picked out in white letters.

The news in the pub was that, ten years after the Great War, when George's father had died in the Zeebrugge raid, owners were building new yachts and needed crews. The huge 'J' class and the big schooners took a couple of dozen hands. Even the comparatively small Six-Metres had a professional crew of two, a skipper and a foredeck hand.

Like most of the Harbour boys, George had grown up in small boats. He reckoned he could take one to windward as well as any of his friends. He knew the feel of a sailing boat in a tideway – that magical balancing act between wind and water, and the signals a tiller transmits to a helmsman's fingertips. The pressure of a weather helm on a reach when the hull heels to a gust. The sudden slackening of rudder against water when the jib is taken aback as a new slant of wind starves the sail of its motive power. That strumming as the wake slips astern and the tiller hums.

The idea of crewing on one of the racing yachts at Cowes was inviting. Now that his father was dead, he had to support his old Mum. There wasn't much money in the fishing or wildfowling. A break from hauling nets would make a welcome change. What's more, he rather fancied a navy jersey with his yacht's name on it. So one evening George walked over to the other side of Quay Meadow, where his cousin, William, the boatbuilder, had his cottage. He had been a hand on the old King's *Britannia* and would know the ropes. William was encouraging and said he'd put out some feelers. He had to go across to Cowes, anyway, to get some bronze mast fittings from Pascal Atkey, the chandler, for a smart little cruiser he was finishing off in the yard. He'd have a word with one or two of his old mates.

Ten days later, he met George by the Raptackle on the Quay. He'd spoken to one of the old Solent skippers called Cundy about George looking for a berth. Cundy was quite a character. He'd started long before the war, as the lad who did all the worst jobs aboard one of the big schooners. He liked to tell the tale of his first owner, who used to have his breakfast on board before a race. The skipper would come down to the saloon, cap in hand, and say, 'Forgive me, my lord, but might you care to come up on deck and see the start?'

From the schooner, Cundy had graduated to paid hand on the little Half-Raters, skimming dishes, grossly over-canvassed, that battled at close quarters with each other all the way round the course.

It was in those seasons that Cundy had learned the secrets of how to work the Solent's tides and eddies. For the past three years, he had been skipper of one of the crack Six-Metres. Tiny and tough, known throughout the Solent as something of a martinet, Cundy put the fear of God into the hearts of most of his competitors. You wouldn't want to push your luck with him on port and starboard. Fiercely loyal to his owners, he was never afraid to tell them what he thought of their tactical sailing. He loved to win.

Cundy told George's uncle that he had just been obliged to sack his crew – an awkward cuss, who argued the toss about tactics in the middle of a race. Cundy couldn't have that: in the pub afterwards, maybe, but not half way round the buoys. He wouldn't let even the owner do that! So the lad got his wages (and kept his jersey) but he'd have trouble finding another berth, at least in the small world of the Solent skippers. Cundy hadn't found a replacement yet – the crews' union knew him for a hard man – so he was ready to give young George Appleton a trial. He liked to train up his crews the way he wanted them. In fact, he preferred to take a raw hand and teach him the ropes, after his own exacting fashion.

'No promises, mind. But let's have a look at the cut of his jib.'

On a bright April morning, with a gentle Westerly filling in, and the sun bringing out the pots of varnish in the yards along the river, George stood on the edge of the hard on the Hamble, hailing the ferry to take him out to Cundy's Six-Metre on her mooring. The skipper was fitting a set of wooden battens to a new Ratsey mainsail. The ferryman sculled his boat alongside, fending off with his boathook. He knew he'd have to stand Cundy a pint or two if he even kissed the yacht's paintwork. Cundy winked at the man and looked at George. He seemed strong enough.

'Come aboard, but take your dirty shoes off first.'

'Aye, aye, Mr Cundy.' George nipped lightly on to the teak deck.

'So, you're young George Appleton, are you? I knew your father. We served in the same ship.'

'I never knew that, Mr Cundy.'

'There's a lot you don't know, son. For a start, just call me Skipper. Stow your kitbag up forrard, clear of the sail bags under the foredeck. You may need to get at those sails in a hurry.'

Cundy spent the next hour showing George the ropes, the layout of the rigging, how the spinnaker pole stowed, and the Highfield levers for the running backstays. George marvelled at the bronze sheet winches for grinding the foresail in, bone-tight.

How clean everything was after the mud and fish scales of the harbour boats!

Cundy was enormously proud of his vessel. Her name was *Sandiana*, called after the names of her previous co-owners' wives, Sanchia and Diana. She had been built up on the Clyde just before the War. Thirty-six feet overall and, so it seemed to George, astonishingly narrow in the beam, her lead keel drew over five feet. The varnished mast soared on and on upwards, setting 440 square-feet of sail. Her brightwork gleamed.

'That's the fresh water and a shammy leather after every race. Keeps her nice and shiny, so the owner's happy. Then we put the canvas covers over the forehatch and the cockpit to keep the varnish smart.'

Cundy stood by the mast.

'Let's go for a sail. It's good weather for stretching the main.'

They bent the new sail on the boom and hoisted the creamy canvas to the masthead, making sure the tack and luff were not stretched too tight. George cast off the mooring and Cundy took the yacht close-hauled down river to the entrance to Southampton Water.

Once clear of the Hamble, *Sandiana* met the sea breeze. For the first time in his life, George felt the thrill of a beautifully balanced racing hull, eating its way to windward. How different *Sandiana* was from the lumbering working craft of Chichester Harbour!

Out of the corner of his eye, Cundy watched the young man's reactions with approval. He had the makings of a sailor, and he'd soon enough pick up the tricks of the trade. By mid afternoon, it seemed to George he'd hoisted and lowered the big genoa and the spinnaker a hundred times. Not quite so many tangles now and he began to know where everything lived. They bore away for home and Cundy, cuddling the tiller under his elbow, lit his pipe.

Back on the mooring, Cundy offered George the berth. They shook hands on it that evening, over a pint. Cundy's wife found a room for George in the village, with the widow of an old tugboat skipper who took in a lodger. Over the next fortnight, Cundy made George sweat, practicing his sail drill until he halved the time it took him to set the spinnaker after rounding a mark on to a run. He was even trimming the sail in his dreams. Every day, he learnt something of the mysteries of those heart-breakers, the Solent tides. How to get them to work for you, before the others had noticed that the inshore eddies along the Island turned before the main stream. How to nudge the yacht to windward, by lee-bowing the current. How far you had to aim above a mark of the course to allow for an adverse flow. And the appalling strength of the ebb at Springs, roaring down to the Needles.

The first race of the Cowes season was on the Saturday. The programme showed the start at eleven o'clock, from the Squadron line. They had sailed *Sandiana* over from the Hamble earlier that morning in a fresh Westerly breeze, and were jilling around off the Squadron steps, waiting to pick up the owner thirty minutes before the ten-minute gun. The club launch, all gleaming chrome and varnish, brought her gently alongside, as Cundy held the yacht into the wind, mainsail shivering.

Lady Anthea Tollemache had outlived her beer baron husband by twenty years. She wouldn't dream of admitting to being seventy ('Nearly grown-up, dear, that's all.') and she was still quite a girl, an impression heightened by the tight little blonde curls peeping out from under her yachting cap. She still looked elegant under her yellow oilskin. George couldn't help noticing (he wasn't meant to help it) her long legs in sea boots, stepping across to *Sandiana*'s deck. But nor could he fail to notice the wrinkles on her cheeks under the two bright blobs of rouge.

Cundy's wife had confided in George over tea that Lady Anthea had started off in the second row of the chorus in the old Gaiety revue. She had led a long succession of protecting gentlemen a merry dance, casting them all aside, but never losing their friendship. Old Tollemache had been smitten and had taken her sailing, only to find, rather to his surprise, that she had loved it, proving herself a natural helmswoman. When he died, while losing in the casino at Le Touquet, his widow had kept *Sandiana* in commission, with Cundy as skipper. She took a house every summer at Bembridge ('For the grandchildren, you know – they love the shrimping.') and was a popular character in the Six-Metre fleet, flirting disgracefully with all the retired officers who formed the bulk of the class owners.

She was, Cundy conceded, a natural, with that feminine delicacy of touch and instinctive feel for the magical interplay between wind, water, sails and hull that put a select band of women in the prize lists. Cundy had confessed she was a magician at taking a boat to windward in a fluky breeze. Trouble was that, when it blew, in close company with other yachts, she flapped. She relied on her skipper for tactical advice, having difficulty making up her mind. By the time she had decided when to tack, it was generally too late. Her opponents were quick to exploit this temperamental weakness.

What happened was that, when Lady Anthea was able to sail her own race and concentrate on making her boat go fast through the water, she was often unbeatable. Given a blow and under tactical pressure with other boats at close quarters, however, the old girl could go to pieces. So *Sandiana* sometimes finished up near the bottom of the fleet. It made Cundy wild.

Poised on the side deck, with Cundy holding her steady, Anthea waved to the other members in the launch and stepped down into the cockpit. She looked George up and down. George reckoned those faded blue eyes didn't miss much. She gave him a grin as Cundy introduced her new hand. She had rather nice dimples, he noticed.

'Welcome on board, George. Cundy will tell you, you'll have your work cut out looking after *Sandiana* and me. But we're worth it!'

George was starting to blush when Cundy told him to hoist the working jib. Cundy showed Anthea the course. She took the helm, reaching up and down the start line. The tide would be taking them down to the windward mark, West Lepe, south of Lymington. But the wind was against tide and the Solent, especially off Cowes, was already lumpy. *Sandiana* pitched into the sea, sending off a shower of spray to leeward. A dozen other Sixes were wearing their racing flags, their ensigns stowed. Cundy suggested a starboard tack start, for safety, at the outer end of the line. The Squadron cannon boomed out the five-minute gun and the Blue Peter broke out on the flagstaff. Cundy checked his stop watch.

'Keep a sharp lookout to leeward, laddie.'

They ran off a bit and gybed round a couple of times. Then, sheets slightly eased, they headed for the line. Boom!

'A lovely start, Ma'am.' She'd got the best of it: nicely up to windward of the fleet, with a clear wind.

'Now just you sail her and don't bother about the others!'

They carried on close in to the Green and tacked to get into the stronger tide off Egypt Point. George, squatting under the cockpit coaming, could see they were well clear of the second yacht. Lady Anthea certainly knew how to sail. Gradually they increased their lead until they were off Salt Mead Ledges. George was watching Cundy measuring the angle for the moment to tack, in time to lay off the course for rounding West Lepe. It had to be judged nicely, or else the tide would sweep them the wrong side of the buoy. Anthea saw her skipper looking.

'Shall we tack now, Cundy?'

'No, Ma'am, not yet.'

Pause.

'Say when, Cundy.'

A long pause.

'Not till I say, Ma'am.'

'Surely it's time, Cundy?'

'That's about it. Tack now, Ma'am.'

'Oh Cundy, are you sure?'

'For God's sake, go about, woman!'

After a long moment's hesitation, Lady Anthea put her helm down and *Sandiana* gathered way on the new tack. George was amazed at how the ebb had carried her below the mark.

'Bear away, Ma'am, or we'll go the wrong side.'

The flap was on. She frantically bore away as Cundy paid out the main sheet and George eased the jib. *Sandiana* was surfing on a broad reach, desperately trying to claw back to leave the buoy to port. George saw the buoy straining at an angle to the force of the tide. It seemed inevitable, almost as though a hidden magnet was drawing the yacht to hit. They very nearly squeezed past. But the angle was wrong and their quarter just scraped the mark.

'Oh, Ma'am. You left it too late!'

'Oh, shit! We've got to retire. Lower that racing flag and we'll go home. I'm so sorry, Cundy. And your first race too, George. You must think me a duffer.'

'Never you mind, Ma'am, there'll be plenty more.'

They ran back to Cowes in silence and picked up a temporary mooring off the Island Sailing Club. The boatman took her ashore and Cundy and George sailed *Sandiana* back to the Hamble.

They cheered themselves up in the pub later. Several of the rival crews were there. One of the hands was obviously well tanked up. He staggered over to them and laughed in George's face. 'Your owner, my son, was better in the chorus line than at the helm.'

George put his pint down and eased off his stool by the bar.

'Why don't you just bugger off.'

'Or what'll you do, sonny?'

George hit him hard on the jaw and the man folded up on the floor. The other men laughed and one of the older skippers said, 'I reckon he had that coming to him. But don't make a habit of doing that, lad, not in this pub.'

'I'll see he doesn't,' said Cundy, pushing George back to his stool. 'Or else you'll be looking for another berth.'

He stood George another pint and, after they had taken a few sips, turned to him with a twinkle.

'Mind you, I'd have done the same if he'd laughed at me. We have to stick up for the owner. She's a good girl.'

That was the moment when George began to feel a proper member of *Sandiana*'s crew. He was not entirely steady when he got into bed that night, but he was happy. As he dropped off to sleep, those faded blue eyes were twinkling at him.

Sandiana did much better over the rest of the season and finished, to George's pride, up in the prize money. Cundy and he made a good team, and Anthea was pleased with them. Her skipper she valued as an old friend, even when he called her 'woman' in moments of stress. As for young George, she grew fond of him; almost motherly. She liked the way he tried not to blush when she looked at him; on hearing about the incident in the pub on the Solent grapevine, she appreciated his loyalty.

During Cowes Week, *Sandiana* lay on a mooring in the harbour. Cundy stayed with his sister who lived up the Medina. George found digs in the town.

One day, when racing was cancelled because it was blowing Force 8, Anthea asked George to come back to Bembridge for the afternoon to meet her family: the grandchildren were staying. George didn't like to refuse. The chauffeur drove them back to Bembridge in the Rolls.

George took a change of clothes in a kitbag with him and wallowed in an enormous Victorian bath when they arrived. The daughter and the young twins had just come in from shrimping. They had tea on the lawn and he helped the boys peel their boiled shrimps. The family went out of their way to be nice to him while he tucked in to the home baked chocolate cake. After a time, he relaxed.

They asked him to tell them about himself. Before long, he found himself talking of his life in the Harbour, of the wild nights after the duck and the shoals of bream that came round from Bognor in the summer. He spoke about his mother and the family boatyard; of his hope that, one day, as his uncle had no children, he might be needed to take the yard on. But boatbuilding needed a bit of capital and it wouldn't be easy.

After tea, the twins showed him how to play croquet. Before he knew it, the time had come to go. He thanked Anthea and promised the boys a morning aboard *Sandiana*, teaching them their knots. He was driven back to his digs, sitting rather straight in the back of the Rolls. He'd enjoyed his tea – more than he thought he would. The owner and her daughter had been very decent. But it had made him uneasy – the silver teapot, those cups and saucers on the lawn, and the maid handing round the scones in her starched cap.

In the evening, Anthea spoke to her daughter about the young man. They agreed he was a good lad. The twins obviously regarded him as an ally. Anthea told the story of how he had stood up for her in the Hamble pub. She knew about young men. That one had a touch of quality. The girl who got him would be a lucky one. He ought to do well. But he'd need a helping hand to get him started with his boatbuilding.

That autumn, when *Sandiana* was safely chocked up under cover in her yard on the Hamble, Lady Anthea spoke to her family lawyer. She had inherited everything when her husband died, and had more than enough for herself and her family. They were all very well provided for. Beer money, she called it. She instructed the lawyer to set up a trust fund for George. Not a fortune but a decent sum, to be paid out annually for the next twenty years. She wouldn't notice it herself, but it could make all the difference to that young man. The solicitor raised no difficulty. He was used to his client's acts of occasionally wayward generosity. In fact, he rather approved.

George helped Cundy stow *Sandiana*'s gear in the shed and wash her sails in fresh water. They shook hands and arranged when to meet to fit out the yacht the following spring.

George went back to Bosham and his mother on the Trippet, and back to the old routine of wildfowling.

By the winter, he was seeing quite a lot of Sally, a dark-haired Chidham girl whose father worked on the farm at Cobnor. The family lived in one of the tied cottages on the estate. Her parents approved of young George. They didn't think much of his prospects, however, and tried to discourage Sally from seeing too much of him. But Sally had come to enjoy being with the young wildfowler. They always seemed to have so much to talk about. She often managed to meet him of an evening by the Raptackle on Bosham Quay, when they were loading and unloading the trading ketches lying alongside. He used to walk her home beside the creek, and they told each other of their hopes and fears.

Just after Christmas, when the snow lay on the Downs, something unusual happened: George had a telegram. It was from Cundy. He'd never had one before, from anybody. He read it out loud to his mother: 'Lady Anthea dead stop please telephone'.

He put on his jacket, went to the telephone booth at the end of the lane and put his pennies in.

Mrs Cundy answered: 'Oh, George, thank you so much for phoning. Cundy's so upset. Hold on, I'll get him.' Cundy came on the line.

'Hullo, George, thanks. It's bad news, I'm afraid. The owner died yesterday.'

'What happened?'

'She'd been playing charades with the twins and had a heart attack. When they got her to the cottage hospital, she was dead. I'll be going over to the funeral in Bembridge the day after tomorrow. The family's selling *Sandiana*.'

'I'll come with you.'

'You don't have to.'

'No, I'd like to. She was good to me.'

George met Cundy on the ferry pier at Southsea and they took the bus over to Bembridge from Wooton Creek. The church was full. It looked as if all the Solent owners were there, with several of the skippers, too. They sang 'For those in peril on the sea'. George remembered those moments of panic rounding a mark, her acts of kindness and her grin.

Afterwards, as Cundy and he were walking out of the churchyard, an elderly man in a wing collar caught up with them and introduced himself.

'Forgive me, but am I right in thinking you are Mr George Appleton? Might we have a word?'

Cundy tactfully moved off and the man gave George his card: 'Thomas Edington Esq., Solicitor', with an address in Chancery Lane.

'I am the late Lady Tollemache's legal adviser. I have to inform you that, under the terms of her will, you are the beneficiary of an annuity which she has settled on you from her estate, payable annually over the next twenty years. The sum involved is £1,000 a year.'

George was stunned. He asked the lawyer to repeat what he had said.

'There must be some mistake. She was my owner and was very kind to me. But I didn't really know her at all well. Are you sure?'

'Quite sure. She made rather a point of caring for people she liked, who deserved to be helped. You're one of them. She wanted you to benefit under her will. Let me have your address and, when all the legal formalities are complete, I shall arrange for payments to be made on the first of January every year.'

'I don't know how to thank her, or you.'

'You don't need to,' smiled Mr Edington. He liked the way the young man had taken his news. 'All I'm doing is carrying out Lady Anthea's last wishes.'

George caught up with Cundy and told him, with wonder in his voice, what he had just heard. Cundy patted him on the back.

'I'm glad for you, boy. I've *also* to thank the owner for her generosity. Let's go home and drink to her.'

They did, back in Hamble, and when Mrs Cundy had helped them carefully both to bed that night, she prayed, like the

116

good Methodist she was, that their benefactress would know of their gratitude.

When he got home to Bosham, he walked over to Sally's cottage at Chidham and told her his news. She took his arm and smiled up into his face.

'I'm so happy for you, George. I think you deserved it.'

They told her parents. It was amazing to see how suddenly Sally's young man had become a welcome suitor.

The next day, George told his uncle, who made his nephew sit down in the parlour. He spoke to him, for the first time, specifically about his plans for the future of the yard. Since he had no children, he had been hoping for some time now that George might eventually succeed him in running the yard. But he had been getting increasingly worried. The boat-building business depended on the health of the economy. When there was a slump, people didn't order new yachts. The days of the big crews, anyway, were past: they were just too expensive. A yard like his was better adapted for building small craft. The fishing punts and harbour work boats had been their staple. But there weren't the fish in the Harbour nowadays. Many of the boats were not being replaced. The fact was that both fish and jobs were scarce.

All the same, he wasn't too despondent. The trend now, certainly in the Harbour, was towards the smaller sailing boats. Several sailing clubs had established themselves over the past few years. They all had their regattas and their class racing. The cruisers starting to take moorings in the Bosham and Itchenor reaches all needed tenders. He was convinced there was a future in turning out the Chichester Harbour Restricted Classes, eighteen-, sixteen- and twelve-foot long, and the little scows that all the Solent harbours were sprouting. He had been hearing about the young Cowes designer, Uffa Fox, who had begun to draw a revolutionary fourteen-footer hull that planed off the wind on top of the water. The young would love that. But it would mean converting their traditional practices to much lighter hulls, more delicate work, higher finishes, and laying down batches of clinker hulls.

Capital would be needed to handle the boat-building techniques for this new market. George now had some money.

If he was ready to chip in, he'd make him a full partner now. He would teach him the trade – he already knew a lot about the business, having spent most of his holidays helping in the yard. In the nature of things, he'd have to bow out in a few years time, and then George could take the whole thing over.

'How about it, George?'

George stood up and hugged his uncle.

'I'd like that more than anything else in the world.'

Interlude

NIGHT ANCHORAGE

The little yacht had ghosted down channel from Cobnor to East Head near the mouth, as the sun was setting. She just carried her way against the last of the flood tide. Above the Hayling shore the sky flamed, fading softly, burnishing the mirror of the sea.

Hoitak was a Vertue class sloop, twenty-five-feet long overall, and built thirty years earlier in Hong Kong. She was built to last, in best Burma teak, and her owner was very proud of her. He went forward and prepared to anchor, while the mate put the helm down and brought the yacht round into the lazy wind. It was almost high tide and the water lapped against the dry sand of the Head.

Five other yachts were at anchor. The skipper let go in three fathoms, thirty yards off the beach. The breeze had died and the tide had not yet turned, so *Hoitak* lay at rest, her anchor chain hanging straight down.

They stowed the mainsail, gathering up its belly and pulling it aft along the heavy boom before tying the sail down into a neat roll. They coiled the sheets. The skipper lit the paraffin riding light and hoisted it and the black ball, high in the rigging above the foredeck. The lamp was an old friend: it would stay alight all night long, whatever the weather. When all was secure for the night, the couple sat in the cockpit, watching the stars come out, listening.

It was a perfectly still night. They heard the plop of a bass jumping as it hunted along the shallows. Over towards Pilsey came the piping of an oyster catcher. Snatches of conversation floated across the water from one of the other boats. Apart from that, silence. The night grew chill.

They went below, lighting the gimballed brass lamps in the saloon. The cabin looked cosy and welcoming. Soon after supper, they tucked themselves into their bunks and chatted in the dark. *Hoitak* rocked gently as the first of the ebb shifted the anchor chain on the sandy bottom. Moonlight flashed down through the companion-way hatch, shining on the varnished lockers. The water made happy gurgling sounds against the hull.

The skipper put his head out of the hatch for a last look round. Hardly a breath of air. The first dew had dampened the deck. East Head loomed dark and the channel marks blinked red and green up and down harbour. He shivered and pulled the hatch shut before wriggling down into his sleeping bag again. He listened to the tiny sounds of *Hoitak,* chuckling.

Chapter VIII

LITTLE SHIPS

Looking back on it, that Summer of 1938 seemed to go on for ever. Bright cloudless days and the gentle sea breeze filling in before noon. As the junior in a barrister's chambers in Lincoln's Inn, Charles Appleton had taken his fortnight's holiday after a busy year. He was staying with his parents in the old cottage at Bosham, where he had grown up. His father, George, had given up the wildfowling – not enough birds about is what he said, but Charles knew it was really arthritis that kept him ashore. The duck punt still lay on the saltings at the top of the creek. George carefully bailed her out every day. He had made a success of the boat yard, employing a dozen men. His little cruising yachts and clinker dinghies had a fine reputation in the Harbour.

Where Charles got his brains from, nobody quite knew. He had gone on from the village school to Chichester. From there, he won a Postmastership to Merton, the first of the family to go to university. On the advice of his old classics master at Chichester, he had opted to read Law, and had never regretted it.

He used to stay with an aunt in Clapham during the vacation. Every morning, he took the bus to the Law Courts in the Strand. The ushers would tell him which Court promised the best action that day. They were used to law students sitting-in on the cases in King's Bench. They based their advice not so much on the substance of the case as on the personality of the judge hearing it. Charles was fascinated by the theatre of it all: the fencing between the opposing advocates, the dry humour of the best judges, and the surgical logic of their summing up.

In his third year at Oxford, Charles had the good fortune to have a tutor who so fired his enthusiasm as a legal scholar that he managed a First in his Finals. His Warden gave him a recommendation that opened the doors of one of the leading chambers in the Inns of Court. Having eaten his dinners, he was now taking all the briefs the Clerk in Chambers put his way. He shared digs near Covent Garden with another young lawyer.

Every summer, Charles spent as much time as he could sailing his twelve-foot Chichester Harbour Restricted Class dinghy, *Penguin*, built by his father as a prize for the scholarship. For three summers he had camped in the field at Cobnor on the Oxford University Yacht Club's marine week. The lady members had cooked sausages and made endless mugs of tea on a primus. They used to take their picnics down to East Head in a convoy of little boats. Charles had grown up mudlarking in the Harbour. For him, it would remain a special place.

One summer, he had been asked to crew in one of the new International Fourteen-Foot dinghies at Itchenor. He put his baby Seagull outboard on to the transom of his own dinghy and went over there from Bosham early every morning of Itchenor Week, in time to help rig the Fourteen before the start.

The Fourteens had established themselves at Itchenor a few years earlier, their young owners bringing boats down from Norfolk, because they found the open but sheltered waters of the estuary a perfect place to race. The older dinghies, often designed by Morgan Giles, had been dramatically overtaken by Uffa Fox's planing hulls.

There were now sixteen of the beautifully varnished examples of the Class lined up on the staging of the Club. By 1936, the Fourteen Footers were well established there. That year, the Club presented the Class with a solid silver tankard, called the Itchenor Gallon. It attracted to the line thirty-seven starters from all over the country. The race was won by one of the top local helmsmen, Stewart Morris, in *Alarm*.

At the end of the race, Charles decided to save up and ask Uffa to build him a new dinghy for the following season. That winter, he met Uffa in his houseboat on the Medina river at Cowes. Uffa liked his enthusiasm and called him 'Nipper'. Yes, he could build him a boat. Once he got his lads on the job, and if the Nipper supplied the beer, he'd have it ready for Easter. Stewart Morris and Peter Scott had just ordered new ones. He'd have a production line soon! He wanted to give his new design a slightly flatter run aft and deeper shoulders to the hull, to get it lifting quicker on to a plane. And lightness – lightness was all. What about a wooden centreboard? You only needed weight in a steam roller. Charles became Uffa's disciple and took delivery on time. He called his dinghy *Pintail*.

After racing her that first season, capsizing twice off Deep End, he felt he was beginning to know the boat's ways. He and his crew were working together as a team, using their weight to sail her upright; learning to bear away, jib eased a trifle, to get *Pintail* up on to a plane. It was a thrill in a whole sail breeze, several Fourteens alongside, screaming along, wakes flattened out astern, trying for an overlap at the next mark. Perhaps the best of all for Charles was the delicate finger-tip work of taking *Pintail* to windward in light airs, tacking gently out of the tide, taking advantage of the wind shifts. Tactical racing at its best. Bare feet on varnish warmed by the sun, and the dry mainsheet in his hand, elbow tucked against his body.

But it was too good to last. Despite Mr Chamberlain's 'Piece of paper' after Munich, Charles and most of his friends had become fairly sure that they would have to fight Hitler before long. They waited, making the most of the summer of 1939.

It was a memorable August. He was staying in the Club. One still morning, he had walked down to the end of the jetty before breakfast. The flags drooped against the flagstaff. Under the jetty, as the tide came in, the big mullet were shading themselves. A fair-haired girl in shorts and a white shirt was sculling a tender to the jetty from a moored cruising ketch. She brought the little boat gently alongside and Charles took her painter. She had come ashore to fill a can with water. She thanked him and their hands touched as Charles handed back her painter.

That day's race also stayed in his memory. It was to be the last for a long time. His crew had arrived after breakfast in his yellow MG with the cracked leather seats. They rigged *Pintail*, standing their mugs of coffee on the sea wall separating the club lawn from the stage. They'd need the big genoa this morning. It was still a flat calm. Charles slipped the wooden battens into the cotton mainsail, soft and warm to the touch. He checked the course and his stop watch, then they wheeled *Pintail* down to the water.

'Bang!' The ten-minute gun.

124

Twelve starters, jilling around upstream of the club line. Not much room between the moored X-Boats and Sunbeams. All the old faces in the other boats: Stewart, wearing his posh yachting cap. David Pollock with a new crew. Charles Currey in a borrowed dinghy. Half the fun of the Fourteens was the company of the other helmsmen, and the continuous experimenting with new ideas: Peter's trapeze, with his crew standing on the coaming to keep *Thunder and Lightning* upright in a fresh breeze; Ralph's joystick for levering the jib in tight and keeping it there; Stewart's low-cut foresail to lower the sail's centre of effort when it really blew.

By the five-minute gun, it was clear that the fleet would be aiming to start out of the tide, right up to windward on port tack. Charles knew the breeze would be coming in soon. He'd seen the darker ruffles on the water down by Deep End, half a mile ahead. With fifty-five seconds to go, he came in towards the Itchenor shore, close hauled on starboard, putting one dinghy about. He tacked a yard out from the end of the jetty, his centreplate just grazing it. He was close behind Stewart, and two other boats were a couple of yards astern.

'Bang!' The start. And a second gun, because someone was over the line. A good start. Get her sailing. Don't pinch. 'Ease your jib a bit.'

It was always fluky in the lee of Itchenor. The mainsheet tightened in his hand as a finger of wind filtered between the cottages and Haines yard. *Pintail* was moving nicely through the water, beautifully balanced. No need to sit her out. He pulled his floppy hat over his eyes: the sun was very bright. Off Cobnor, still hugging the south shore, for the first time they felt the true sea breeze.

Another dinghy was trying to creep up astern to windward of him. He edged up slightly, giving them a distorted air flow. The other boat, starved of wind, dropped back and tried to break through to leeward. Good. That seldom worked. Charles luffed up whenever he could, trying to keep as far out of the tide as possible. They'd have to go about soon and start short-tacking up the edge of the channel as it swung southwards. Suddenly *Pintail* seemed to go dead. Probably some weed on the plate. Up and down with it. Yes, a great gob of the stuff, freed from the centreboard and drifting astern. Two boats had passed him. Damn.

'Cool it, Charles.' You had to stay calm if you wanted to race a boat right.

'Ready about!' Look under the boom. A nice little gap.

'Lee Oh!' Shorewards on starboard until the plate touched on the mud – it was shallower by that corner.

'Up a fraction.' She'd hardly lost way. Then about again.

The fleet spread out past Thorney entrance. *Pintail* was lying fourth. All still to play for. Never relax until you hear the finishing gun. Where was the East Head mark? Hard to see in the glare. There. A bit nearer in than he'd thought. He sailed well up tide of the mark – he'd learnt that the hard way. The boat astern was coming up to the mark on starboard tack. They were pinching to make it against the tide, while *Pintail* was sailing nicely, slightly off the wind. He'd just clear them ahead. Close!

'Nearly had you!' called her helmsman.

'Miles off,' grinned Charles. The boat ahead had misjudged the strength of the tide and touched the mark while rounding. Bad luck. To have to retire when you did that was maddening. So Pintail was third now, Stewart, about thirty yards ahead and David, lying second.

Wind and tide with them, they shot down to the mouth of the Thorney channel in no time, sheets eased. Through the Thorney goal posts on a lovely broad reach, the genoa lifting the bows just off a plane. He'd be gybing round the Thorney mark. Leave it wide. Boom across. A close reach back up the channel to the mouth. Not a bad Sou'wester now. Bearing away.

'Up spinnaker.'

The blue and white sail blossomed and *Pintail* leapt forward on to a steady plane. David's crew was having spinnaker trouble. All tangled. His boat seemed to wallow as *Pintail* steamed past.

Second place! But Stewart probably knew more about making a dinghy plane than anyone. Between Park and Deep End they came on to a broad reach. A good blow now, some spray coming aboard, leaning right out.

Old Tich was drift-lining for bass in his rowing boat off Deep End. He always won the best fish competitions and had often taken Charles out. The bass liked the disturbed water where the Bosham and the Itchenor channels met.

Come on! Concentrate! You don't win races thinking about the fishing. Before they knew it they were opposite Itchenor.

'Spinny down.' Genny up. Sail close up to the club mark. Stewart was sailing up the Itchenor shore. Don't follow my leader. Edge over to the far side. Might be more wind there. Close hauled. Tide strong against them. Agonisingly slow over the ground. Would they do it?

'Bang!' Stewart was over.

'Bang!' Only ten seconds in it.

'Well sailed, skipper!'

'Thanks. Nice spinnaker work. We were coming up on him.'

Back on the stage. Sign the declaration. Second place confirmed. A pint of ice-cold shandy on the lawn. A day to savour.

A month later, war was declared and *Pintail* was put away inside Darley's shed. With a group of his sailing friends, Charles volunteered for the R.N.V.R. After a spell in barracks, he was earmarked as a potential officer and sent to the *King Alfred* training establishment. At the interview, he told them that his first choice was Coastal Forces. It seemed that his experience with small boats helped. By the summer of 1940, he was commissioned and posted to H.M.S. *Hornet*, the Coastal Forces base at Portsmouth.

On his forty-eight-hour leave before joining, he spent some time in his father's yard, looking over the Harbour Defence Motor Launches they were building and picking up as much as he could about their construction. Their double diagonal planking was impressively strong, but his father grumbled about the stream of modifications which the Admiralty insisted on, and the bureaucracy of the naval constructors' department.

Charles was assigned to one of the boats in a flotilla of Vosper Motor Torpedo Boats as a spare hand, learning how the sophisticated little craft worked. His skipper was regular RN and he gave the new boy a slightly frosty welcome. In those early days, the regulars tended to sniff at the 'Wavy Navy' amateurs. The Number One, however, was a cheery yachtsman who made Charles soon feel part of the crew.

The Chief Petty Officer, a small ferret-like man, treated Charles with that special brand of amused tolerance that the best of his kind reserved for green Sub-Lieutenants, regular or hostilities-only. He was by far the oldest man on board. The ratings, mostly in their twenties, called him Grandad behind his back. The other experienced hand was the Engine Room Artificer, a middle-aged Petty Officer with the perpetual stoop of his trade, who was fiercely protective over his engines.

'Won't she go any faster, Chief?' the skipper had asked during Charles's first outing.

'No, Sir. Not while I'm aboard. We're doing 34 knots already.'

It was the sheer power of the MTB that struck Charles during his training exercises in the Solent. The surge as the engines opened up, lifting the bows high in the air and the V-shaped hull on to a plane. Once speed was cut, the boat sank back into the water, just like a Fourteen. It made him feel quite at home.

The role assigned to Charles's flotilla was to attack the German convoys that crept along the French coast between Cherbourg and Le Havre: the Seine Bay was the MTBs' stamping ground, and night-time was their element. Night operations meant mastering a whole new set of tactics and disciplines, as Charles was beginning to discover. Finding the enemy, keeping in touch with the other boats of the flotilla, fixing your own position and finding your way home. Once they reached an area where a convoy was expected, the boats had to lie in wait until the target was sighted. The trick was to manoeuvre quietly into range, lining up the bows and estimating the angle that allowed the torpedoes to hit. Once the torpedoes had been fired, the sooner you made off at full speed, the better, because the convoys were escorted by destroyers, E-Boats and heavily-armed trawlers. The fate of an attack depended on visibility, the phase of the moon and the sea state.

MTBs were not much good when it was rough. Aiming a torpedo needed a stable platform; in a swell, the little boats bounced all over the place. They had to reduce speed in any wind over Force 4. In bad weather their open bridges became cold and miserable after a few hours. Many of their early actions proved inconclusive. Too often their engines broke down, or they failed to make contact. The Channel weather sometimes forced them to head for home. Twice, Charles's boat spent a horrible night towing another MTB back to Portsmouth from mid-Channel. One time, it was afternoon before they berthed alongside, and the crews of both boats were half asleep.

After a year with the flotilla, Charles's Senior Officer had him into the office to tell him he had done well. He was going to give him a month's experience in the Operations Room. Then he'd be due a week's leave. After that, a second wavy stripe and how would he like a boat of his own? Charles sang bits of HMS *Pinafore* as he walked back to the wardroom. His skipper must have thawed. Come to think of it, they'd got on rather well recently.

Next morning, the duty driver took Charles up the hill to the headquarters overlooking Portsmouth Harbour. He reported to the Commander in charge of the shift and was introduced to the Joint Planning Staff. They shared an office next door to the Ops. Room, where a large table, covered with a giant chart of the Channel, filled the centre of the room. Wrens, like croupiers at a casino, with long pointers were shifting various wooden symbols on the table, each one representing the position of friendly and hostile ships and aircraft. One of the planners explained how it was like a game of three-dimensional chess. You had to anticipate what the enemy units would be doing. What they knew about the enemy might be based on actual sighting reports or top secret intercepts of their radio messages. Sometimes, details of convoy sailings came from reports by agents in occupied France. The intelligence staff had to collate the various pieces of the intelligence jigsaw and produce a daily assessment. That was flashed to the units at sea and the RAF squadrons, as well as to the coastal forces at their bases, like *Hornet*. The planners used the intelligence as the framework for deciding how best to attack the enemy. Charles was impressed by the way the ethos of attack lay at the forefront of everything he saw that day; how the MTBs were at the sharp end of the offensive operations.

When a coastal forces sortie was launched, the Captain (Coastal Forces) would take his place in an armchair overlooking the table. He had a direct secure line to the C-in-C, Channel, and a RAF liaison officer nearby. His job was to whistle up air cover and rescue operations when needed. Charles thought the whole atmosphere was very professional. You felt the teamwork, as well as the tension, rising around the table if our ships got into trouble, and relief and elation if an enemy symbol was shuffled off the board.

That morning, they were preparing for a night attack on a convoy which intercept reports had revealed was due to sail from Brest at sundown. Another flotilla from *Hornet* had been earmarked and they had been spending the morning fuelling and loading torpedoes. Six boats would be going out. Two Hunt class destroyers were moving into mid-Channel in support. A squadron of Typhoon fighter-bombers from Thorney Island was on stand-by. The Met. Office were forecasting nine-tenth cloud cover and a Force 3 South-Westerly. Radio frequencies were issued. The CO of the flotilla was briefed, and the boats left harbour at 1500 hours, aiming to lie in wait for the convoy, ten nautical miles north-east of Brest, at 2200 hrs.

Charles quickly realised that waiting was the name of the game in the Ops. Room. Long hours, endless cups of coffee, waiting for the first reports. Wireless discipline meant these would be very brief, even by the standards of a naturally laconic Service.

That night, things went wrong. The convoy was protected by an unusually strong escort group. The news came back in a broad Devon burr: 'Boats separated after attack. We're down to 4 knots. Skipper and all on bridge wounded. Will need support. Don't quite know ETA.'

The Ops. Room went into high gear and the Duty Officer sent a signal back to the damaged boat to say they'd have all the back-up they needed. Charles went back to *Hornet* in thoughtful mood.

Two mornings later, Charles came into the Ops. Room and noticed a pretty new face among the Wrens at the table. She had a head-set over her fair hair. He looked again. It was. The same freckles. It was the girl who'd smiled at him from her dinghy off the Itchenor jetty. He had thought about that face. When the shift on duty changed, he came up to her in the wardroom as she was pouring herself a cup of coffee.

'Forgive me. You won't remember. But I think we've met.'

She looked at him. 'I do. You tied up my dinghy one morning at Itchenor.' She smiled the same smile.

They chatted about the Harbour over their coffee. Charles asked if he might take her out to supper one evening. They arranged to meet and the restaurant in Southsea did its best on the rations. Charles hardly noticed the menu. The evening passed far too quickly.

Her name was Deborah Bentley. Her father was a surgeon and they had a holiday cottage at Itchenor, opposite Darley's sheds at the end of the street. They had kept their ketch, *Myrmidon*, on one of the moorings in Itchenor reach. She wanted to hear all about *Pintail* and the Fourteens, and to learn about Charles's work. She proved a good listener. They found that they could talk easily to each other, and they shared a love of the Harbour and sailing. She seemed as sorry as he was when they said goodnight outside her quarters at the base.

They went out together several more times during Charles's month in the Ops. Room. On one sparkling October afternoon, they walked along the turf on the ridge of the Downs, with the Nab tower, the Island and most of the Solent spread out below them. Deborah congratulated him on getting his own MTB.

When he kissed her goodnight the evening before rejoining his flotilla, she wished him good luck and asked him to take care of himself, for her sake. He walked back to his cabin, on air.

There had been a delay in the delivery of his new boat, while Vospers carried out some last-minute modifications. Charles spent the next four months as the flotilla's spare officer, standing in for

people on leave or away on courses. He went out in different boats, doing various jobs and learning a lot in the process.

In February, he was told to take a damaged Motor Gun Boat over to one of the Chichester yards for repair, as all the Portsmouth yards were working overtime. Charles was delighted to hear the work was to be done at Itchenor Shipyard and that he was to supervise the job.

When he next met Deborah, he told her the news. She suggested he should stay in their cottage. She had been on duty over Christmas and the New Year and was due a week's leave. She could take it while he was there. He asked how her parents would feel about that. She grinned.

'Daddy's quite emancipated. If he doesn't mind, Mummy won't. And he'll do what I ask. Anyway, they'll probably be down for the weekend themselves. I know he wants to get the cover off *Myrmidon* and see she's all right after the worst of the winter.'

They agreed it was a happy coincidence that the MGB would be lying in the same yard as her family ketch. The cottage was only round the corner.

Deborah got her leave, went over to Chichester by train, bought some provisions and caught the bus to Itchenor. The cottage felt cold and damp when she went in. Nobody had used it since early November. But her father had stacked some logs in the shed. She soon had the wood stove going in the sitting room, giving out its friendly roar. She made a pot of tea and stretched in front of the stove. The prospect of the week ahead was wonderful. She wanted to make it good for Charles. On the phone, her parents had been fine about having him to stay. In fact, her dear Dad had said he'd heard so much about him, it was high time they met. They'd be down for the weekend.

On the Tuesday, Charles was due to bring the damaged boat round to the Harbour. It was a filthy winter's day, gusting in wicked bursts up to Force 6, sleet cutting visibility right down. Part of the MGB's bridge had been shot away and her steering gear was giving trouble. They would only be able to make about 8 knots. All the deck crew and those on the bridge put on as many layers of clothing as they could manage: woollen underwear, heavy jerseys, oilskins, seaboots and towels around their necks to stop the drips. Once clear of Portsmouth entrance, they met wind against tide and the icy spray swept over the bridge. By the time they reached Horse Sand Fort, the crew on watch were soaked. A Tribal Class destroyer, showing off as usual, overtook them at speed. They had to turn bow on to stem the wash. Conditions improved slightly as they bore away once round the Fort and set an easterly course for the Chichester entrance. Wind and sea now came up their backsides.

Off Langstone, they dipped chunks of bread into mugs of hot pea soup. Charles went below for a moment to look at the chart. He plotted their estimated position: about three miles, or half an hour, to go before they should be up to the Bar Buoy, marking the southerly tip of the West Pole sand which jutted out from the Hayling shore, guarding the western approach to the entrance. On the other side, the Winner sand stretched well out to sea. It would be half flood when they crossed the Bar: a good seven foot of water under them. But it wouldn't be easy to spot the buoy in this murk.

Half an hour later, they still hadn't picked up the mark. Every time Charles swung his binoculars in an arc ahead, the lenses were smeared with sleet, and visibility was down to about one hundred yards. He couldn't afford to overshoot and find himself, like so many vessels over the centuries, aground on the Winner, not even on a rising tide.

Suddenly the starboard lookout sighted the buoy, further to seaward than Charles had expected. The flood must have carried him further inshore than he had allowed for. He maintained course until the Bar Buoy lay just to the south, then ordered the Cox'n to steer due north. That should bring him up to Eastoke Point and the deep water of the entrance channel.

The last time he had entered the Harbour was in *Pintail*, that August before the war, on a spinnaker run after rounding the windward racing mark out in Hayling Bay. He'd been in shirt sleeves on a sweltering afternoon. It seemed an age ago.

The towel around his neck was sopping and the MGB wallowed in the swell as they came in over the bar. What a rotten entrance it was! By now, it was getting dark, earlier than usual. Still no sight of the shoreline. He reduced speed and could hear the breakers on the beach to port.

Then, out of the gloom, came the port-hand beacon of Eastoke Point. The tide swept them up the channel, past the terns diving into the froth. He could find his way home now, blindfold. Past the northern edge of the Winner, where the sandbank drops off so quickly into deep water, up to East Head. Each mark of the Harbour had its memories.

'Reckon you've done this before, Sir,' chuckled his Cox'n, as Charles conned the boat through the murk.

'Yes, Cox'n. Once or twice. But never in anything longer than fourteen feet.'

Past Roman Landing and Thorney. No Park racing mark nowadays. Ease her round to starboard. Deep End and the Bosham channel to port. The wind had dropped now, and the sleet had turned to rain. Charles wiped his face with the towel. His clothes under his oilskins felt damp. Itchenor reach ahead. Charles was amazed at the number of landing craft on the trots near the shore. Several small boats and a Harbour Defence Motor Launch lay alongside the Itchenor Shipyard pontoon. But there was just room for them to squeeze in on the upstream side. He let the current carry him past the end of the jetty and nudged alongside. Mooring lines and springs, fore and aft.

He'd brought a bottle of rum with him and the crew crowded into the mess deck, steaming, and they finished the bottle between them. They tidied up the chaos that is the legacy of a rough weather passage in a small vessel. Charles reported their safe arrival.

He saw off the crew in a Navy bus sent round to take them back to Portsmouth. Two of them, the Engine Room Artificer and the Leading Telegraphist, would be living on board to keep an eye on their boat while under repair. Dockyard mateys were always eyed with suspicion by the Navy. Charles told them they might do quite well to have meals in the village pub. He guessed that during the week the yard had estimated it would take to complete the repairs, most of their pay would go into the bar till.

He picked up his canvas grip and walked in the dark along the muddy path to Deborah's cottage. He raised the dolphin knocker and she ran to the door.

'You're frozen. Come and get warm. The stove's going.'

She helped him off with his stiff oilskins and he changed into some dry clothes in front of the fire while she boiled the kettle. It was snug in the little living room. She brought in the tea tray and filled two pottery mugs with Lapsang Souchong.

'Your clothes will soon dry on the Rayburn, and the water's hot for a bath before supper.' After tea, when Charles had to tell her all about his trip, she led the way up the narrow stairs. 'We've only got the two bedrooms, I'm afraid. But there are hotties in the beds. You're in here, if that's all right.'

'Perfect.'

'Shout if you need anything'.

Charles laughed. 'I may spend the whole time shouting.'

'That wouldn't do at all. I'd have to rock you to sleep.'

'I'd like that.'

For supper, they had grilled bass that Deborah had bought from the fishmonger in Chichester, with a bottle of Muscadet her father had brought back from a Channel cruise. Afterwards, they sat in front of the wood stove and gossiped. Charles found it hard to keep his eyes open and she watched him nodding.

'Bed,' she said firmly. When they got upstairs, the oil stove in Charles's room had gone out and it was quite chilly. Deborah glanced towards her door and, hesitating, said, 'You might be warmer in with me.' Charles looked at her. She was blushing.

'I think I might be,' he said gravely. He put his arms around her waist and they kissed.

'Come,' she whispered.

The next three days were pure delight for both of them. A time of discovery; sharing their past and their hopes for the future. Although nothing specific was said, they assumed that it would be a future together.

Charles's supervision of the repair work was made much easier when he found that the foreman at the Itchenor yard had started as an apprentice under his father at Bosham. He spoke warmly about him.

'Now don't you fret yourself over your warship, Lieutenant. My boys will see to her – and I'll see to them if they don't! By the end of next week you wont be able to see where the dents were.'

His two crewmen were being spoilt by the barmaid at The Ship. The workmen from the yard were taking their breaks in the MGB's cabin, hearing tall tales about night actions in the Channel, as they gulped the strong Navy-issue tea with tinned condensed milk. Sensibly, Charles let them get on with it.

Tuesday's storm had passed and the rest of the week was bright and cold. Deborah took him on her favourite walk along the coastal path down to East Head. They sat, bundled up, on Charles's oilskin on the grassy verge under the holm oaks, watching the curlew and the oystercatchers feeding in the mud. One afternoon, they went to the cinema in Chichester. Afterwards, they sat in the nave of the Cathedral, listening to a choir practice. But most of the time, they just wanted to be alone.

Before they knew it, Saturday was on them and Deborah's parents arrived for tea. Their meeting was much easier than Charles had feared. She had phoned her mother the day before and Charles guessed she had told her how things stood between them. Anyway, he got a hug from a beaming mother. Richard Bentley put an arm around his shoulder and, while they toasted crumpets on the wood stove, made him talk about the Fourteens.

The repairs were ahead of schedule, and by the following Thursday, the grey paint had dried. The foreman had been as good as his word: when Charles ran his hand along the woodwork, he couldn't tell where the mend was. With Deborah, he stood the team from the yard and his two men a pint in the pub at lunchtime, reporting to *Hornet* that the boat was ready. Her crew arrived by bus the next morning and got the boat ready for sea.

Deborah came down to the pontoon to see them off. Charles looked astern as they eased out of Itchenor reach. She looked very small at the end of the jetty, waving.

A cold day, but calm with brent geese on the saltings. The Harbour to themselves. Astern, Stoke Clump, that old leading mark, skylined on the crest of the Downs. Down harbour and over the Bar, the Nab etched on the horizon. Round the Bar Buoy and course 260° Magnetic to the gap between the Forts. A new Midshipman had come along for the ride. Charles handed over to him and went below to eat a bully beef sandwich for lunch. It had been a very special holiday and he would always remember the face of his girl on the jetty, waving her red scarf.

That trip was certainly the end of the holiday for Charles. He took delivery of his new command, MTB68, an improved version of the old Vosper boats: more powerful (and reliable) engines, a pom-pom in an armoured turret mounted in the bows, twin Oerlikons aft of the bridge and four torpedo tubes. On her trials in the Solent she touched 30 knots. Nearly all the crew were hostilities-only men. His old Petty Officer had come with him to the new boat.

Coastal Forces had developed a style of their own, adapted to life in the little ships. It was informal, less stratified. Charles quickly built up a spirit of a mutually supporting team, proud of their vessel. Two of the ratings were Chichester harbour men. One had rowed the summer ferry between Itchenor and Bosham Hoe; the other was one of the hands working for the Harbour Master. The rest included West Country fishermen, a deckhand from the Solent car ferries and a giant Scotsman who had shot salmon nets on the Tweed estuary and he spent his spare time spearing mullet below their pontoon. His two other officers were yachtsmen who proved both competent and good company. Together they made a fine crew.

They all had a lot to learn about their boat and about each other, and Charles made them work hard during the following month's trials. At the end of the work-up, the Senior Officer came out with them for the day's torpedo practice and pronounced himself satisfied. From now on, MTB68 would be fully operational.

By this stage of the battle of the Narrow Seas, the Royal Navy had begun to dominate the Channel. By day, having air superiority made all the difference. But the outcome of night-time actions, when the coastal forces were busiest, could never be taken for granted. Sod's Law often applied.

Over the next six months, Charles and his MTB68 won their spurs on offensive operations in the Channel. By the end of the summer he had, in fact, become one of the most experienced officers in the flotilla. One September morning, while the boats were preparing for that night's patrol, Charles was summoned to the flotilla office. Captain, Coastal Forces, was sitting there with his Senior Officer. He greeted Charles and told him he'd done well and that he'd put him up for a Mention following his brush with a pair of armed trawlers the week before. He'd be sending him for a spell as an Instructor at the Tactical School.

Before that, he wanted to see if Charles would be interested in a special operation that was coming up. It was secret, and involved one MTB taking a couple of Motor Launches with 30 Commandos aboard over to France to raid a new radar station. The raiding party would be going ashore in rubber boats. They'd do their job quickly and quietly. Then the trick would be to leg it as fast as possible. The MTB would have to cover the MLs' rear. There'd be a destroyer waiting for them further offshore. But there would be some tricky minutes when the balloon went up, as it was bound to when the radar was blown up. It wouldn't be easy, but as the radar was of a type that the boffins were extremely anxious to know all about, the risk was justified. Would Charles be prepared to volunteer for the job? Charles looked out of the window on to the pontoon where his crew were loading torpedoes. Yes, of course they'd do it. When would it be? The Captain said the party would need a week to practice their drills and to get to know the three little ships. Weather conditions would be critical.

Two days later, the Senior Officer Introduced Charles to a young Commando Major in the wardroom.

'Charles here will be shepherding your people in and out.'

They had a drink at the bar and Charles liked the look of the soldier. They'd spent the past few days practising launching their rubber dinghies from a Motor Launch, and the Major said his party would be ready to go as soon as the Met. Office gave the word.

That afternoon, the two MLs arrived at *Hornet* and Charles met their skippers, both trawler captains and obviously competent seamen. The next day, the commandos embarked. One of their officers was an Admiralty radar specialist. He briefed Charles about the German equipment. They thought the Germans had beaten the allies in the race to produce a more powerful set that dramatically extended radar coverage in the Channel.

'We want to see what they've been up to. Quite badly, actually.'

'Hence our raid,' said the Major. 'The radar station we're after is on Barfleur Point, just east of Cherbourg. That whole stretch of coast is cram jam with defences. So the whole show depends on stealth, and speed. We've got to have a pitch-black night and no sea. We creep in, set a timed fuse on the equipment to go off when we're well clear, then scarper like the clappers.'

Charles smiled. 'Sounds a bit like the cat that crept into the crypt, crapt and crept out!'

Over the next four days, the Met. people forecast too much moon. The waiting made them all a bit edgy. Then a front moved in and conditions for the following night looked just right: a light southerly breeze, new moon, overcast, with slight drizzle — and a calm sea. Charles had tea with Deborah in the canteen and it was obvious she knew about that night's operation. They didn't talk much. They weren't alone.

'Take good care, Charles, for me.' He promised.

After breakfast the next day, Charles held a briefing meeting with the two ML skippers and the Commando officers. He kept it brief. They all knew what they were doing. But he did impress one thing on them.

'Once you've got the raiding party back on board, don't hang around. Leg it for home. I'll be riding shotgun behind you.'

When he'd settled details with the two other captains, Charles asked the Major if he wanted to add anything. The soldier thought for a moment.

'No, I don't think so. We've practised the launching drill and the bit on land is up to us. The great thing will be to keep quiet throughout the performance. The only other thing is that I'm very glad my people are in your hands.'

They walked down to the pontoon. The two Motor Launches were rafted up to the MTB, Charles noticed that all the commandos were down below, out of sight of prying eyes. It would be stuffy below deck.

'Cast off. Slow ahead.'

The Senior Officer was on the pontoon to see them off. 'Good luck, Charles. Remember what the cat did!'

Charles lifted two fingers to him in salute. The two MLs formed up astern and Portsmouth Point slipped past.

What naval departures that Point had seen over the centuries! Ships slipping out, often to make history in every ocean. And how Rowlandson had stopped the place from becoming a pompous legend with his cartoon of the lewd enticers on the Hard, robbing the tars of their pay when they came ashore!

Off the Nab, Charles set a course to take them ten miles off *Pointe Barfleur*. His little convoy made a comfortable 15 knots. Halfway across, they met their covering destroyer as planned, patrolling the approaches to Cherbourg. Her Aldis lamp blinked 'Good hunting' and Charles sent back their thanks. Apart from friendly aircraft overhead, nothing else was sighted. The drizzle started and night fell sooner than usual. Around midnight, the crew had some meat-and-two-veg. stew in bowls, with the inevitable strong, sweet tea.

Charles buttoned up the neck of his oilskin. A wetting sort of rain, but it cut the visibility a treat. When they were, by Charles's reckoning, about four miles off the coast, the MLs came along either side of the MTB, the rubber dinghies were inflated on deck and launched. The commando party clambered down into them. Their faces were blackened and they wore black cap comforters. They carried Thompson sub-machine guns or Stens, grenades and knives. One section had backpacks with the explosive charges. The Admiralty boffin and his assistant were unarmed but packed specialist instruments and tools. A pair of enormous thugs had been detailed off to give them close protection.

Charles called over to the ML skippers to make their best speed home and took the four large rubber boats in tow, making a silent 5 knots through the calm water. Searchlights and distant crumps from the direction of Cherbourg showed that the RAF had begun their diversionary air raid to occupy the Germans' attention. Sea and land were equally black. Nothing to be seen.

When Charles judged they were about 500 yards offshore, the rubber boats cast off and paddled silently towards the beach. Charles cut his idling engines and they lay still on the calm surface of the water, waiting.

It was very quiet. They could smell new-mown hay and rotting seaweed. Half-past two. Nothing seemed to be happening ashore. Three-quarters of an hour dragged by. Long minutes. If things had gone according to plan, the dinghies should be back soon. Charles ordered the crew to be ready to start up in a hurry. Then he saw a torch flashing nearby. All four rubber boats came alongside. The Major climbed up to the bridge, smiling.

'All's well. No alarm. We clobbered the guard – half of them were kipping. The boffins got the bits they wanted and the charges are laid. The lads will be on board in a minute.'

The commandos climbed up the netting hanging over the side of the hull and filed below to squeeze into the mess deck and gulp cocoa. Most of them were soon fast asleep. The crew hauled the rubber boats over the transom and deflated them. Charles ordered Full Ahead. MTB68's bows lifted as she roared up on to a plane. They must have been heard ashore. The MLs would be well on their way by now. It felt fine to be moving again, and at their proper speed, though with her load of men the hull rode rather lower in the water than usual.

Charles had the telegraphist signal to base the coded message, 'Mission accomplished. All well. Heading home.' After ten minutes, the Major looked at the luminous dial of his watch.

'Should be going off any moment now.' And a minute later they heard, above the roar of their own engines, a series of explosions from the headland astern.

'Well done, the commandos!' Charles thumped the Major on the back.

The Midshipman on the starboard side of the bridge saw them first. Two white bow waves heading towards them at speed. None of our own ships were due in that sector tonight.

'Enemy in sight to starboard!' It looked like a pair of E-Boats on patrol.

They must have been seen by now.

'Gun crews traverse right. Range 300, closing fast.'

'Port ten.'

''Open fire!'

The MTB vibrated as pom-pom and starboard Oerlikon opened up, sending an elegant stream of tracer shells curving towards the targets. The E-Boats turned parallel to MTB68, going astern of her fast. They returned fire and sent up starshell, blinding Charles and his gunners. Most of the enemy aim was high. But, with their last burst, shells splintered the MTB's bridge. Charles was suddenly knocked flat, sprawling on the bridge deck. There seemed something the matter with his head and left arm, though he couldn't feel much. It seemed very quiet. The firing must have stopped. He felt himself being lifted. Then everything went dark.

It was his Cox'n who carried Charles below. The skipper's arm was shattered and he was bleeding badly from a splinter in his head. The Major came below and helped put on a tourniquet and bandages, while the commando medical orderly gave him a shot of morphine. They made up a bunk for him in the tiny wardroom and the medic kept watch.

Two of the ratings had been slightly wounded, but that was all. There were no more incidents on the passage home. Their escorting destroyer picked them up halfway across. Charles's Number One sent a signal back to base, reporting the brush with the E-Boats and that the skipper had been wounded. He'd lost a lot of blood and would need a hospital, and fast.

A reply came straight back, ordering them to make for Chichester Harbour to save time, as the Portsmouth hospitals were

all full and there was room at nearby St Richard's. An ambulance would be waiting at Itchenor. The MTB laid a course for the Nab and made her landfall by dawn. The rain had stopped and the sun had broken through.

Back at *Hornet*, the Senior Officer of the Flotilla had called Wren Bentley over to his office. He knew about Charles and his girl. She had already heard in the Ops. room what had happened. The Commander told her to go and meet Charles at Itchenor in the duty van. Deborah stammered her thanks and ran to Charles's cabin to put some things into his grip that he would need in hospital. She only prayed he'd be able to use them.

On board his MTB, Charles had woken soon after daylight, his head and arm throbbing. The medic brought him a mug of tea. When the Number One squeezed into the cabin, he found his skipper sitting up in the bunk, looking white and heavily bandaged, but smiling. He heard the orders for Chichester and that they were just reaching the Bar buoy.

'How you feeling, Sir?'

'A bit groggy. Must be the morphine.'

Charles asked to be helped up on deck. His men bustled around and made him a comfy armchair out of kapok lifejackets right up in the bows. They all knew that Chichester Harbour was his patch. They eased him down into the seat. His arm hurt, despite the pain killer, and he couldn't move it. He wondered if he'd ever be able to handle *Pintail's* mainsheet with it. He asked how the two ratings were.

'Nothing that a couple of pints won't cure, sir,' the Cox'n assured him.

It might have been much worse. And they'd done the job.

With the flood tide under her, the little ship planed through the entrance. What would the old Harbour Master have said about the speed limit? Charles took it all in as they swept past the familiar marks up channel. Bosham entrance to port now and Itchenor ahead to starboard. How wonderful to be back in his Harbour. And was that a girl on the jetty?

ENVOI

Six-year-old John woke early, as the sunlight lit the curtains of his little bedroom in the cottage. Summer, and the holidays before him.

Yesterday he'd found the treasure, the Roman penny. He'd kept it under his pillow all night. But he had to decide what to do with it. He didn't want to lose it out of his pocket. Nor did he want to hide it away in some box. He had found it at the top of the creek, in the mud. It was probably a lucky penny.

As he lay in bed, the thought struck him. It had come from the Harbour, where it had been for hundreds of years. Somehow, it belonged to the Harbour, not to him. What, if he kept it, the coin brought him bad luck? He might not even catch a bass when Daddy came down to Bosham for the weekend and took him fishing. His Dad was a great fisherman, even if he only had one good arm. He'd been hurt in the war and had won a medal.

John made up his mind. He put on his clothes and went to the end of the garden overlooking the creek. The tide was half up. He climbed down the Trippet sea wall and walked out along the wade way until he reached the water, its fingers creeping over the mud. He took the coin out of his pocket. Should he keep it? No. In his heart, he felt it ought to go back. He threw the old penny as far into the tide as he could. He watched it spinning in the air, glinting in the early morning sun. The penny plopped into the water, making a ring on the surface, just like the little fish did down at Deep End.

Postscript

THE CHICHESTER HARBOUR TRUST

I hope this book may have given you a glimpse of the Harbour's past and what makes it such a special place.

If you would like to help protect it for future generations to enjoy, might I ask you to support the Chichester Harbour Trust?

It was set up as a charity in 2002. It's objective is:

> to acquire land, sites and buildings within the Chichester Harbour Area of Outstanding Natural Beauty and its setting of landscape, environmental, recreational or historic value and to promote the conservation, protection and improvement of the natural beauty and the wildlife of the area for the public benefit.

To find out more about the Trust, go to our website:

www.chichesterharbourtrust.co.uk

If you would like to make a donation, it should be sent to:

The Administrator,
Chichester Harbour Trust
PO Box 327
Chichester
West Sussex,
PO19 1ZN

Telephone: 01243 777632